Marketing Policies
for Agriculture

Marketing Policies for Agriculture

JAMES R. BOWRING
> *Professor of Agricultural Economics*
> *University of New Hampshire*

HERMAN M. SOUTHWORTH
> *Professor of Agricultural Economics*
> *Pennsylvania State University*

FREDERICK V. WAUGH
> *Director, Agricultural Economics Division*
> *Agricultural Marketing Service*
> *U. S. Department of Agriculture*

1960
Englewood Cliffs, N.J.
PRENTICE-HALL, INC.

PRINTED IN THE UNITED STATES OF AMERICA

55771C

Preface

The problems of agricultural marketing are becoming more important and more difficult as time goes on.

Today's concern with agricultural marketing is due in part to the existence of enormous and costly surpluses. Thus, one of our greatest current needs is to expand markets at home and abroad.

But even if we solve our surplus problem completely (whether by production control or by expanding markets), our agricultural marketing problems will continue to grow more important and more difficult. This expectation is due in large measure to the rapid urbanization of our people, to the increased specialization of our farms, and to the higher real incomes of our consuming population, leading to a demand for new products, better packages, and improved marketing services.

Our marketing problems of the future can be solved only if farmers, businessmen, administrators, and Congressmen make sound economic decisions—decisions that will be profitable to farmers, to marketers, and to consumers. Sound judgment on matters of this kind requires a good, workable understanding of economic principles. For that reason, we have emphasized economic theory and principles; this volume is not intended as a compendium of facts and statistics about agricultural marketing.

There is room for considerable disagreement concerning many of the issues discussed in this book. In many cases, we have taken rather extreme positions or we have made provocative statements. This practice is intended to encourage discussion. We hope that the readers of this book will think for themselves. It is quite unimportant whether they agree or disagree with the authors. In any case, the judgments expressed in this book are not intended as authoritative doctrine. Nor do they represent the official views of the University of New Hampshire, the Pennsylvania State University, or the United States Department of Agriculture.

We hope that this book will interest many readers in the growing problems of agricultural marketing, and that it will help them solve these problems in ways that benefit the farmer and the general public.

Appreciation is expressed to the United States Department of Agriculture for the use of the photographs in this book, which they supplied.

JAMES R. BOWRING
HERMAN M. SOUTHWORTH
FREDERICK V. WAUGH

Durham, N. H.
Penn State, Pa.
Washington, D.C.

Contents

PART 1 · Decisions in the Market

PART 3 · Marketing Policies of Organized
Groups

PART 1

DECISIONS IN THE MARKET

1

Introduction

Some Aims of Agricultural Marketing

Why are you studying agricultural marketing? What do you expect to get out of this book?

Perhaps you have not thought much about these questions. But you should. You will always get more out of a book if you have a definite aim in mind.

Probably some of you intend to be or are farmers and hope to get some ideas that will help you sell your products to the best advantage. Some of you may be processors, wholesalers, or retailers. You will want to know how to build up a profitable business. Others may work for governmental agencies and will want to improve public services, such as market news, inspection and grading, supervision of marketing agreements, and price-supporting programs. Still others of you may have jobs with farm organizations or with trade associations. You will want to know what stand to take on current issues of policy and legislation in the interests of your members. Or you may be legislators. Here, again, you will be concerned with current issues of policy and legislation—but presumably you will want to analyze these matters from the standpoint of the general public interest. Even if you are in some nonagricultural line of work (say, dentistry or astronomy), you are bound to be a consumer of farm products. You should know something about agricultural marketing if you are to buy intelligently, or to vote wisely.

If you should be a college professor, you will combine all of these interests. You will need to help prospective farmers, processors, dealers, bureaucrats, legislators, and con-

3

sumers. So your aims must be very broad. To be a good college professor, or a good Congressman, you must understand the problems of many different groups of people. Moreover, since their interests are sometimes conflicting, you will have to search for solutions that will promote the general welfare.

The Main Aim of the Individual

The general aim of economic life is to obtain a high "real income"—in other words, a high "level of living."

THE FARMER

The individual farmer wants to get ahead, to make money. To do this, he must be efficient. He must use production methods that keep costs down and that bring high crop yields and large output from his livestock. But he must do more than this. He must choose the right things to produce in the first place—the crops or livestock products that will bring him the largest return in the market. And then he must choose the time, place, and method of sale that will bring him the largest net return for what he has produced. In other words, he must have one eye on production but must keep the other eye always on the market, for many of his most important decisions are marketing decisions.

THE HANDLER

The processor or dealer likewise seeks to make money. This aim similarly requires achieving high technical efficiency, whether in slaughtering livestock and packing meat or in milling wheat or soybeans or in operating a supermarket. Costs must be kept down and spoilage and waste must be kept to a minimum. But here, also, marketing decisions are just as important—where and how much to buy, when and where to sell, what prices to pay, and what prices to charge. The firm engaged in processing or marketing farm products aims both for a large volume of business and for a good profit margin on each unit it handles, because it is the product of volume times unit margin that determines the firm's gross return. Also, the firm wants to keep costs down.

THE CONSUMER

Consumers of farm products have a different problem, although an analogous one. They seek to get the most satisfaction from their expenditure for food and clothing and to do so with the least outlay of time and money. This goal likewise involves technical efficiency in the running of a household: the things that are bought must be used to best advantage to get the most out of them. But the successful housewife is aware of the importance of her marketing decisions in determining how well her family gets along on its income. Even in a matter so routinized as food buying, she watches for bargains. She, likewise, faces problems of what, where, when, and how much to buy.

COMMON AIM

Farmer, processor, dealer, consumer, all are concerned with this main aim of economic life—with making money and with getting the most for their money. Don't scoff at this pursuit of the almighty dollar. There is nothing wrong with it. When we are engaged in economic activities, we all pursue the dollar, the pound, the yen, or some other kind of money. Of course, it isn't the money, as such, that is important. It is what money will buy. It is food, clothing, housing, education, amusement, and many other good things of life which we call real income. But, to get these things, the individual needs money. And he works mainly for the purpose of earning money. This does not minimize the importance of enjoying one's work and the possibility thus of achieving more satisfaction than one would in some less agreeable occupation that paid more money.

The Main Aim of Society

Man is a social animal. He is interested not only in his individual welfare and the welfare of his family: he is also interested in the welfare of *groups* of people, and of society as a whole.

Here, again, the economic aim is to increase real incomes.

But here we are concerned with the real income of a group of people rather than of an individual. Also, we are concerned with the distribution of income within the group.

The group may be small or large. It may include all tobacco growers in the Connecticut Valley. It may include all meat packers in the United States, all persons in the South, the whole population of the United States, or even the whole population of the world. (Some day we may have to be concerned with interplanetary problems. But we shall not cover them in this book.)

Whether the group be large or small, its aim is to increase its total real income and to see that this income is widely distributed within the group. This is the general economic aim of farm organizations, trade associations, governments, and such intergovernmental agencies as the United Nations.

Sometimes the aims of the group will run counter to the aims of some individuals. The group cannot tolerate business methods that seriously reduce the total real income of the group, even though they might enrich a particular individual or corporation. The group must concern itself with such matters as the maintenance of honest trade practices, the suppression of harmful monopolies, the disposal of agricultural surpluses, and the promotion of international trade.

As a citizen and voter, you will certainly have an interest in many of these broader economic problems. They are often difficult. They involve judgments concerning economic policies. This is a controversial field. Here you will often find honest differences of opinion, even among the experts. This book will not give you any final answers. It will not tell you how to vote. But the authors hope that it will suggest points of view that will help you think constructively about the economic problems of groups of people concerned with the marketing of agricultural products.

Problems and Decisions

It is well to keep this broad aim in mind as you study agricultural marketing. But in your day-to-day economic life you will be confronted with a series of specific, practical problems. You will have to make thousands of decisions, some minor and some very important. How can you analyze these problems, and make sound decisions?

The great bulk of our decisions are made unconsciously, or with so little thought that we are scarcely aware of having faced a problem. As the English economist, Phillip Wicksteed, put it, "Habit or impulse perpetually determines our selection between alternatives without any reflection on our part at all." [1] This is true both for individuals and for large corporations and other organizations. And it is well that it is so. If all the things we did required conscious thought—or, in a corporation, specific action by the board of directors—we would do very little. Rather, we would find ourselves in the plight of the centipede who suffered a nervous breakdown in the attempt consciously to direct the movement of each of his many legs.

But the very fact that so many of our decisions are made below the conscious level makes it important that we develop the right habits, that our automatic reactions be the result of wise training based on sound knowledge. Again to quote Wicksteed, "If we are moderately wise, we pretty generally act without reflection in the manner which reflection would have dictated." [2] One thing you have the right to expect from this book, or from a good course in marketing, is that it will furnish you a background helpful in making routine decisions wisely.

INCOMPLETE KNOWLEDGE

Even those problems that do force themselves upon our consciousness—or perhaps especially those—frequently have no sure solutions. This is peculiarly true of economic problems generally and of marketing decisions in particular. To know for sure what is best to plant, the farmer would need

---

[1] Philip H. Wicksteed, *The Common Sense of Political Economy*. London: George Routledge and Sons, Ltd., 1933 (rev. ed.).
[2] *Ibid.*, p. 36.

to know what the weather will be in the growing season and what prices will be at harvest time. To know for sure the best amount of meat to put in storage this winter, the packer would need to know how prosperous consumers are going to feel when they face the meat counters next summer. Even the housewife who splurges on some early strawberries one week because they have come down somewhat in price may regret not having waited when she sees how much cheaper they are the following week. Most marketing decisions involve guessing the future—which can never be known for sure.

Many marketing decisions involve guesswork in judging the quality of products bought or the prices offered or asked by alternative purchasers or suppliers. In principle, it is possible to obtain information on such matters if we are willing to pay the cost. But to sample and test every lot of goods purchased can be expensive. And to explore in detail all the available alternatives in every market transaction can take a great deal of time, energy, and money.

IMPROVED MARKET INFORMATION

In the United States much progress has been made in taking the guesswork out of agricultural marketing. Standards of weights and measures, standards of identity, minimum quality standards, and grade standards help us know what we buy. Relatively high ethical standards in business, plus laws to prevent fraud and dishonest practices and to enforce contracts, give us confidence in those with whom we deal. Numerous private firms or organizations furnish market information. The Department of Agriculture and co-operating state agencies maintain elaborate services for crop reporting, market news, and outlook analysis, to make available to farmers and tradesmen reliable marketing information on which to base their decisions.

NO ONE DECISION IS THE BEST FOR ALL

But, in the nature of things, guesswork remains, and always will remain, in marketing. Hence, we can seldom be sure except by hindsight which decision is best in any particular case. Another aim of this book, however, will be to show how to analyze typical marketing problems so that you can tell what information is most important for solving them, where knowledge leaves off and guesswork begins, and some ways to protect yourself against the harmful consequences of bad guesses.

What the right decision is often depends upon the point of view. All of us are aware of internal conflicts in trying to make up our minds. We want many things but can afford only a few: which are most important? It is of the essence of economic problems that they force us to choose what we shall give up.

Similarly between individuals and between groups, what benefits one may hurt another. In the early days of rayon, for example, much shoddy material was sold. The product generally was given a bad name that took the industry years to live down. Presumably, the manufacturers of the poor merchandise made money, at least for a time. Their decisions may have been "right" from their individual, short-run viewpoints, but they were "wrong" from the viewpoint of the industry as a whole.

CONFLICTS AMONG GROUPS

We have gone a considerable way in the United States in setting up rules, practices, and responsibilities that bring individual, group, and social aims into line. But newspapers daily carry items illustrating the never-ending problems of conflicts in economic interest. In agricultural marketing we continue to struggle against monopolistic practices. Farmers recurrently face the problem that their individual decisions on production may result in total supplies of many products too large to bring a satisfactory return in the market.

A further aim of this book is to bring out some of the differences in points of view regarding marketing problems, the sorts of conflicts that arise from them, and some of the possible ways of resolving these conflicts.

In short, this book is about the kinds of agricultural marketing problems that require the making of decisions by individuals or private firms, by organized groups, and, finally, by public agencies. Of course, no book can analyze all marketing problems for all people—much less show the "right" decisions with respect to all these problems. But the authors have tried to discuss the main types of problems and to bring out the main economic principles useful in analyzing and understanding them and in helping the individuals or groups concerned to reach wise decisions regarding them.

Since policy amounts in practice to our collective day-to-day decisions, it is as wise or as foolish as those decisions collectively.

What Occupation?

One of your first, and most important, marketing problems will doubtless be to study the market for your own services. Since this problem does not fit easily into the body of the book, we shall discuss it briefly here.

Are you going to be a farmer, a processor of farm products, a government worker, a professor, or what? If you already know the answer, do you know why? Did you carefully study the opportunities open to you in various lines of work, and make a decision based upon facts? If not, you should get a low mark in economics. The choice of an occupation is the most important economic decision you will ever make. And once the decision is made, it will be hard to change.

Probably many of you have not yet decided on your future occupation. What do you need to know in order to make a sound decision?

Essentially, you need two kinds of information.

First, you need to know your own capabilities and weaknesses, your own likes and dislikes. Don't take over your father's dairy farm if you hate cows. And don't go into economic research if you are weak in economic theory and statistics. This advice may seem too obvious, but it is strange how many lives are futile because it is overlooked, or because the analysis was superficial. Bear in mind that the "you" of 5, 15, or 25 years from now will be a different person from the you of today, and imagine if you can what he may be like. Which present likes and dislikes are deep-rooted and enduring, which based on temporary responses to transient experiences whose effects time and maturity will erase? Which abilities and weaknesses are inherent in your personality, which reflect the results of passing enthusiasms, or the lack of previous opportunities to test and develop your potentialities? What things are permanently vital to your happiness, and what might you be willing to sacrifice for the sake of a larger money income and the satisfactions that it could buy? In analyzing yourself, in other words, you must *forecast* what you may become—a tricky problem and one that calls for the most sober reflection plus such help as you can get from those with experienced judgment of the character and potentialities of young people.

Second, you need to know the prospective markets for yourself. What jobs might be available to you? How much money could you expect to earn, now and in future years?

Remember that you are selling yourself. Study the possible markets for yourself at least as carefully as a Georgia farmer would study the possible markets for his peach crop. You will find that your study is harder than that of the peach grower. His product is standardized and graded. The radio and the newspapers provide him a great deal of information about prices and market conditions.

You will have much less information about markets for yourself. He is forecasting the market for a season—or at most for the bearing life of his orchard. You are forecasting for your lifetime. What will our fast-growing and rapidly changing world be like 25 years from now? What occupations will it need more of, what less? No one can know for sure, but there are trends that can be analyzed. Find out all you can from your professors, from farmers, from businessmen, from government officials, or from others that may know of possible openings for you.

And don't be dismayed that the problem has no sure solution. That is the nature of economic problems. All of your classmates face the same difficulty, whether they are aware of it or not. Only try to "hedge the risk," as we say in Chapter 15, by developing some basic abilities that can be put to alternative uses and will help make you adaptable to future change.

QUESTIONS FOR DISCUSSION

1. How can your aims as a consumer conflict with your aims as a producer?

2. List the influences which will affect your decisions to buy or sell a product.

3. Do you advocate a goal of the highest money revenue as the basis for choice of occupation? Support your answer.

4. What would you consider to be the main elements of a satisfactory "level of living"?

SUPPLEMENTARY READING

1. Thompson, F. L., *Agricultural Marketing.* New York: McGraw-Hill Book Company, Inc., 1951, Ch. 1.
2. *The Yearbook of Agriculture, 1954.* Washington, D.C.: U. S. Department of Agriculture, pp. 2-21.
3. Stewart, Paul W., and J. Frederic Dewhurst, *Does Distribution Cost Too Much?* New York: Twentieth Century Fund, 2nd ed., 1948, Ch. 1.
4. Marshall, Alfred, *Principles of Economics.* New York: The Macmillan Company, 8th ed., 1936, Ch. 2.

2

Basic Functions of Marketing

Chapter 1 stated that the main aim of this book is to "give you some useful ideas" that will "increase your ability to make a good living," and to "suggest points of view that will help you think constructively about the economic problems of groups of people." More specifically, it aims "to discuss the main types of agricultural marketing problems and to bring out the main economic principles useful in analyzing and understanding them and in helping the individuals or groups concerned to reach wise decisions regarding them."

It is almost a truism that our likelihood of reaching wise decisions is greater the greater our understanding of the situation within which our decisions are made and of the consequences of those decisions. In a book on agricultural marketing, therefore, it seems desirable to start by asking broadly what agricultural marketing is and what it does, whose decisions are involved in it and what depends upon their decisions. That is the purpose of this chapter.

Viewpoints on Marketing

Again as pointed out in Chapter 1, a great many kinds of people are concerned with agricultural marketing, and it can therefore be looked at from many points of view. To farmers, it is the means of changing their products into money income, to get back their production expenses and to provide living expenses for their families. To the large numbers of people engaged in buying and selling, processing, transporting, storing, and distributing farm products, it is what they do for a

13

living. To consumers, it is the source of foods and other goods
that they need and want.

Looked at from the viewpoint of society in general, however, it is the system by which a nation is fed and clothed and
supplied with many other goods, and by which some 40 per
cent of this nation gets its income.

A System of Independent Decisions

It is characteristic of the marketing of agricultural commodities in the United States that this system operates with
a minimum of central direction and control. No one person,
nor any board or commission of a few people, sits at the head
of the system and directs its operation. Instead, it operates by
the independent decisions of the millions of individuals whose
lives are affected by it.

We say "independent" because the individuals concerned
are free to make choices. No one decides for them what they
must do. Farmers choose what they shall grow and how they
shall dispose of their products. Consumers choose what they
shall eat. And the great number of people engaged in the
work of marketing choose what they shall work at and how
they shall manage their various jobs.

Yet these billions of decisions by millions of different people
cannot be wholly unsystematic. Somehow their decisions must
fit together systematically or the whole process would fall
apart. Consumers would not be able to get the things they
wanted to eat, and farmers would have no market for what
they wanted to grow. There would not be independent freedom of choice because the choices would not be there to
choose among. Without some system that co-ordinates the
many independent decisions, the nation would not be fed and
clothed.

Just how important this system is can perhaps be brought
out by a look at the size and complexity of agricultural marketing in the United States today, with some historical comparisons. In colonial times, most of the people lived on farms,
producing their own food and clothing, except as they depended upon itinerant peddlers for special goods like spices

or hired local millers to grind their grain into flour. The few people who lived in towns depended for food mostly upon the produce of surrounding farms. There was very little agricultural marketing. And by present-day standards, levels of living were low. Similar conditions exist in many parts of the world today. They are what we have in mind when we speak of "underdeveloped countries."

Today in the United States most of the people live in cities. They depend for food and clothing upon products grown in all parts of the country and all parts of the world, commercially transported, stored, processed, and packaged to be conveniently available whenever wanted in local supermarkets and stores. Never in history have so many people had such high levels of living in terms of the goods and services readily available to them. We live in a highly developed, urban-industrial country.

Specialization and Marketing

Two things that have made this possible are technology and specialization. They go hand in hand. Concerning specialization we shall have more to say later when we discuss the "principle of comparative advantage." Here we can describe it roughly as a system under which each individual, instead of producing many things chiefly for his own use, concentrates his efforts upon one or a few lines of production chiefly making goods that others will use. He specializes in what he can do best. And technology provides him the means for doing it better.

Specialization, with the aid of technology, has enormously increased our economic productivity. But it has associated costs. For each one to produce not for his own needs but for those of others, there must be a system of exchange. This is where marketing comes in.

A highly developed, urban-industrial economy requires a highly developed, intricate and far-flung marketing system. It requires markets for the local assembly of raw materials, for their concentration at processing and wholesale supply points, for the retail distribution of goods locally throughout the country. These markets must be linked by a vast network of transportation, communication, financial and credit arrangements, buying and selling agencies, handling and processing firms. Range steers or carloads of California lettuce or of Kansas wheat are exchanged many times between the farms where they are produced and the homes where they are consumed as steaks and roasts or as salads or bread.

Urbanization, Industrialization, and Marketing

To supply food and clothing and other necessities of life to 180 million people is a great and complicated undertaking in any case. In the United States, this many people are supplied reliably, day in and day out, in all parts of the country and in all seasons of the year, and the number is on the increase. They are supplied, not just with the necessities, but with all the great variety of agricultural products that are regularly stocked on the shelves of our supermarkets, department stores, and specialty shops.

Our great metropolitan areas could not exist, let alone enjoy the high standards of consumption prevalent today, were it not for the possibility of drawing upon distant producing areas for their daily food supplies. Technology and specialization make this possible.

Furthermore, not only our great metropolises but also our agriculture is a phenomenon of specialization and technology. "General farming" is the exception rather than the rule in the United States today. Most farmers specialize in wheat, in cotton, in lettuce, in corn and hogs, in dairying—in one or a few related products best adapted to their land and location and the other resources they have available for production. They do not feed and clothe themselves, as in colonial or pioneer days. Rather, they, like the city folk, sell their output and buy their food and clothing.

With modern agricultural science and technology, specialized farmers produce a great deal more than was the case when each farm family produced the many different things needed for their own subsistence. This makes it possible for most of the population to work in other industries. Meanwhile, modern agriculture depends upon our mass-production industries for the specialized machinery, equipment, and supplies necessary for efficient farming—as well as for the products that make up the high levels of consumption of farm families.

Thus, country and city are interdependent parts of the great process of specialization and technological advance that has made possible the high, widely distributed, real income of our economy. And marketing stands at the heart of this process.

Basic Functions of Marketing: Physical Functions

It is marketing that bridges the gap between specialized producers and the mass of consumers. To do this involves two sorts of functions. First there are the obvious physical functions of transporting, processing, storing, and so forth, that are necessary for getting products to the places, in the forms and at the times, that they are needed for consumption. These physical functions are like the original physical production of the raw commodities on the farm itself—they are extensions of this productive process, separated from it only as a matter of specialization.

Allocative Functions

But equally important in marketing are the functions of buying and selling and price-making. In appraising these activities, it may be helpful to reflect that in time of war many foods and other goods are not permitted to be freely traded. Consumers are given "rations" limiting the amounts they can buy. Similarly, at earlier levels of trade, a host of regulations control or "allocate" the amounts of products that can be used for different purposes—such as how much milk and cream can be used for ice cream versus butter and skimmed-milk powder, how much rubber can be used for truck tires versus automobile tires, or how much steel for tanks versus automobiles. In farm production during a war, special campaigns are carried on to expand the production of commodities like milk or cotton in preference to others, like water-melons, deemed less essential to the war effort.

This regulation of production and distribution is, in fact, normal in controlled economies. But in our own economy we like to think that the market does the "allocating." Trade determines "automatically" who gets what products and how much he pays for them. Trade determines how much the producers get for their products and, hence, what lines of production they find most profitable. The market allocates goods in consumption, it allocates incomes, and, in the last analysis, it allocates the use of resources in production. We refer to the buying and selling and price-making through which these things come about as the *allocative functions* of marketing.[1]

The Co-ordination of Independent Decisions

It is in this allocative aspect of marketing that we shall find the answer to the question of what holds together this vast, highly organized, highly technical, highly specialized system by which our nation is fed and clothed. Marketing and trade set the conditions within which the millions of farmers, marketing firms, and consumers make their billions of free and independent choices on what shall be produced and how it shall be used. To the extent that the methods and practices of marketing and trade are efficiently designed and wisely organized, these independent decisions are made to work together so that almost everyone can be well fed and well clothed and can make a good living.

Much of this book, therefore, will be concerned with this problem, both in detail as it applies to individual decisions, and more broadly as it depends upon the decisions of groups

---

[1] Many economists limit the term *marketing* solely to these allocative activities. There is justification for this effort to draw a sharp distinction between production and marketing, but this distinction is often difficult to maintain. Most writers on agricultural marketing prefer to look at the total operation of a wholesaler, for example, recognizing that it has both a physical aspect and an allocative aspect, and that these are closely interrelated.

and of governmental agencies that determine the general rules and methods and institutions by which marketing and trade are carried on.

If you succeed, with the help of this book, in grasping the main principles by which the system works—by which it makes independent individual and group decisions add up to a way in which 180 million people are fed and clothed—you will have gone a long way toward understanding agricultural marketing. And we believe that this understanding should help you to make wiser decisions, both in your own individual problems of living and making a living and also in the marketing problems you will decide upon as a member of private groups and organizations or as a citizen.

The Magnitude of United States Markets

It is difficult for one person to appreciate the immensity of the food production, processing, and distribution industries in the United States. The total wheat supply for the 1959-1960 marketing year was about 2,473 million bushels, of which 1,182 million bushels was the new crop. United States consumers used 500 million bushels, 126 million bushels went for seed and feed, exports took 425 million, and the rest was held over in storage for future use.

The 500 million bushels of wheat find their way to consumers from farms to grain elevators, by boat or train to the mills, from the mills as flour to the bakeries, and from there to retail stores and consumers. Numerous by-products, such as millfeeds, breakfast cereals, and special flours, are also produced. Export wheat is shipped to the ports for loading onto ships.

The total supply of barley in 1959 was 627 million bushels; that of oats, 1,379 million bushels; and that of corn, almost 6,000 million bushels.

In 1959 there were 5,274 million pounds dressed weight of beef, 366 million pounds of veal, 4,523 million pounds of pork, and 319 million pounds of lamb and mutton produced on farms and delivered to consumers. This came from over 9 million head of cattle, 3 million head of calves, 33 million hogs, and 6.4 million sheep and lambs. These animals may be raised on one farm or ranch and "finished" by grain feeding on another before they are finally sold. They are marketed by direct sale to packers from the farm, by auction, and by sale at terminal markets by commission men. The numerous packing houses slaughter and dress the animals for shipment to consuming areas as carcasses. Retailers and wholesalers buy the carcasses and cut them up into steaks, chops, and roasts according to local customs and demands of customers. Sometimes the animals are shipped long distances by rail or truck before slaughter, or they are more likely to be killed close to the point of production and the carcasses shipped in refrigerated or ice-cooled cars and trucks. A minimum of time between purchase and final consumption means that little meat is carried over. Therefore, the firms processing and handling meat and meat products must maintain a continuous operation, and producers must make supplies available all year round.

The poultry industry in 1959 produced over 66 billion eggs, which were cleaned, graded, and packaged for use by consumers in large cities and small hamlets. Commercial slaughter of poultry accounted for over 2,000 million pounds of poultry meat, not counting that which was slaughtered on the farm. Over 380 million pounds of eggs were sold in liquid form and 255 million pounds as frozen eggs. This means that poultry dressing plants provided wholesalers and retailers with a continuous supply of poultry meat kept under refrigeration and inspected for quality and health. Egg-processing and drying plants provided outlets for eggs not hatched or consumed in shell form.

In 1958 there were 20 million dairy cows producing an average of 6,330 pounds of milk and 240 pounds of milk fat per cow. Farmers sold to milk dealers 99,418 million pounds of milk for processing and bottling and 411 million pounds of cream, besides selling 2 million pounds directly to consumers. Of the total milk produced in 1958 (which was a typical year), 22.8 per cent was made into creamery butter, 10.7 per cent into cheese, 13.3 per cent into evaporated, condensed, dry milk, and frozen dairy products, and 4.9 per cent went to make farm butter or was fed to calves, while 48.3 per cent was consumed as fresh whole milk. The highly perishable nature of milk requires protection against contamination and control of temperature at all times. Most milk for fluid consumption must be pasteurized. The industry's responsibility for moving this product with a minimum of storage so that milk is consumed within a few days of production presumes highly efficient assembly, processing, and distribution operations.

In addition to the animal products, over 280 million cases of vegetables were canned in 1958. Over 1.4 million pounds were frozen. Large quantities of vegetables are marketed and consumed in their fresh form, the diversity of production conditions in the United States and the world enabling consumers to buy fresh vegetables all year round, in large part as a result of the marketing and distribution system developed through private enterprise. For example, 266 million hundredweight of potatoes were harvested and sold, as were 18 million bags of beans and 4 million bags of peas. In all, over 20 million tons of vegetables are harvested each year with a third of the crop being processed for later consumption and the remainder consumed in fresh form. There are over 18 million tons of fruits harvested and sold each year.

Farmer co-operatives, independent dealers, and processors arrange for the movement of these vegetables and fruits to terminal markets for resale to processors and to major wholesalers and retailers. The large proportion of fresh produce means temperature control during storage and transportation. Consumers in New England receive fresh carrots from California and consumers in Chicago receive fresh McIntosh apples from New England, while highly perishable lettuce is packed in California fields and consumed in New York.

QUESTIONS FOR DISCUSSION

1. How would you define marketing?
2. What marketing problems exist in the United States today which do not exist in India, Nigeria, or Ghana?
3. How do you allocate your time and money? What principles guide your decisions?

SUPPLEMENTARY READING

1. Bakken, H. H., *Theory of Markets and Marketing.* Madison, Wisc.: Mimir Publishers, Inc., 1953, Chs. 1-3.
2. Boulding, K., *Economic Analysis.* New York: Harper & Brothers, 1955, Ch. 11.

3

Marketing Policies of Farmers

We have outlined in a general way what agricultural marketing is, what purpose it serves, and its importance in our modern, complex, specialized society, in which high levels of living depend upon a reliable and efficient job of supplying food and fiber products. We turn now to look at this job from the standpoint of the individuals who take part in it.

First, the farmer. Marketing is his means of turning his production into money income, and he wants to market his products so as to realize the greatest net income he can. What are the choices open to him and what decisions on his part determine how much he will make?

What to Produce

The first marketing decision the farmer faces is what to produce. This does not sound like a marketing problem, but it is. If the farmer is to make money, he must produce what he will be able to sell at a good price—a price that will cover his costs and leave enough over for family living expenses and savings. If most turkey growers misjudge the market and go in too heavily for turkeys, there will be a surplus of turkeys on the market in the fall, prices will be low, and growers will not make much money. Society will likewise be poorly served because not only will there be too many turkeys, but there will be less of other things that some of the farmers might have grown instead.

How Much to Produce

What more often happens, of course, is that different farmers misjudge the market in different ways. Some plan too much turkey production; others, too little. Supplies and prices of turkeys may be about right from the standpoint of consumers. But the farmers—both those who overproduce and those who underproduce—will make less money than they might have made with better planning.

The great difficulty is that farmers cannot know at planting time or breeding time what the market will be when the time comes to sell. They have to make the best guess they can. They may guess that this year's market will be about like last year's. If last year's production was fairly well balanced in relation to demand, this may be a pretty good basis for decision, since demand usually changes rather slowly for essential farm products. But if production last year was out of balance, last year's market conditions are a poor guide. They lead to the kinds of decisions that result in the cyclical over- and under-production of hogs and cattle and the large year-to-year fluctuations in production and prices of many crops.

Some farmers try to judge the market by guessing what most other farmers will plan to do and then planning to do just the opposite. This method has some merit so long as not too many farmers follow it. If most farmers acted simply on the basis of outguessing one another, like traders in the stock market, farming would become a very risky business indeed.

Market-Outlook Information

The United States Department of Agriculture, state agencies, and private services spend considerable money each year making analyses of prospective supply and demand conditions in order to inform farmers of the market outlook for various farm products as a basis for their production planning. The Department even goes so far as to survey farmers' intentions to plant major crops and to breed pigs, so that the farmers may have some basis for judging each other's plans and be in a better position to modify their own plans accordingly. For some commodities the government announces at the start of the season minimum prices that it will support through making loans to farmers or through buying up market surpluses.

Contract Production

In an increasing number of commodities, forward contracting has become widespread. It has long been the practice of canners and of beet-sugar factories to contract with individual farmers to grow specified acreages of crops for processing. In the range country, livestock buyers often contract ahead of the season for the purchase of lambs or steers. More recently, feed manufacturers and others have developed the practice of contracting with farmers to raise broilers. Such "contract farming" is likewise found in egg production, pig and hog production, the feeding of beef cattle, and other lines.

The price to be paid to the farmer may be specified in the contract. More often it is made to depend at least partly on open-market prices at the time the products are marketed. Contracts often contain specifications regarding quality of product, or specify certain production practices designed to assure the quality desired.

Types of contracts vary widely. But all of them reduce certain risks in marketing, in that they assure the farmer an outlet for his product and assure the contracting agent a source of supply. For our present purposes, they mean that the farmer has made his marketing decisions in advance of production.

When, Where, and in What Form to Sell

For some farm products, like milk, that are produced continuously, production planning may be a continuous process. The dairyman can at any time cull his herd, and he can likewise vary his rate of feeding in response to market conditions. For most farm products, however, the main marketing decisions arise at harvest time. Then the farmer must decide when to sell, where to sell, and in what form to market his product.

The kinds of choices open to him differ greatly among commodities and between market situations. The cotton grower, for example, ordinarily takes his cotton to a neighboring gin to have the seeds extracted and the lint baled, and may make

Courtesy U.S.D.A.

Pick-up trucks of watermelon growers await their turn for loading into railroad cars at the Cordele, Ga., farmers' market. Both ventilated box cars and refrigerator cars are used in shipping melons from Georgia and other southeastern States. Hatch covers in the refrigerator cars are left open for ventilation.

contact through his ginner with prospective buyers of his cotton. If he can afford to wait for his money, or if he is eligible for a Commodity Credit Corporation loan on his cotton, he may hold it rather than sell right away, should he judge that this will bring him a sufficiently better price to more than pay the costs of storage. And if he is a large enough producer, it may pay him to sell the cotton himself on a central market rather than sell to a local buyer's representative. He has no problem of form in which to sell, since the size and type of bale is standardized in the cotton market.

The hog producer typically has a wider range of choices. Depending upon how he sizes up market prospects in relation to his feeding costs, he may sell his hogs early, at lighter weights, or hold them longer and feed them more heavily. He may sell direct to a nearby slaughterer or meat-packing plant, sell on a local auction or other livestock market, or ship his hogs to a central stockyard for sale.

The grower of most fruit or truck crops has little choice regarding time for sale. The products must be harvested when they reach the right stage of maturity and, being perishable, must be disposed of promptly once they have been picked. The grower may, however, have a variety of market outlets to choose from, especially if his farm is near a populated area. In that case it may pay him to set up his own roadside stand —or he may take his product to town, selling it in a local farmers' market or peddling it directly to housewives or to retail stores. He may sell it on a local wholesale market, to a shipper who assembles carload lots, or, if he is a large producer, he may himself ship in carload lots or truck lots to a terminal market. He may also have the alternative of delivering to a nearby processing plant.

Co-operative Marketing

If a farmer belongs to a producer's co-operative marketing association, he may turn his products over to the co-op to be marketed. The functions performed by such associations vary widely from one commodity to another. Some merely act as collective bargaining agents for their members in negotiating prices. Others assemble, process, and ship products. Some even are proprietors of nationally advertised brands. Through co-ops farmers have often been able to offset monopolistic practices of buyers and to raise standards of performance of various marketing services, like providing more careful handling of livestock in shipment.

Co-operative marketing will be discussed in greater detail in Part 3. Here it should be pointed out, however, that participating in a co-op makes certain demands upon a farmer's time and energy and requires him to invest some capital.

Costs and Returns from Performing Marketing Services

This raises the general question of how far it pays a farmer to go, as an individual or through a co-op, in performing marketing services. Obviously, the different selling methods we have described differ greatly in this respect. Perhaps the least in the way of marketing services is illustrated by those citrus growers who sell their fruit on the tree, leaving harvesting itself to the marketing agency.[1] At the other extreme are those producer-distributors of fluid milk who have their own pasteurizing and bottling plants and operate their own door-to-door delivery routes.

Basically, the decision here turns upon comparative costs and returns from the farmer's marketing activities versus other uses of his time, energy, and financial resources. The milk producer-distributor gets a retail price for his milk higher than he could get by selling it at wholesale to a handler. But he has a good deal of capital invested in marketing facilities and equipment that might be invested instead in farm production. And time spent managing and operating his processing and delivery enterprise is time taken from the management and operation of his farm. He must ask himself the question, "Will I get a better return on my capital and labor employed in marketing than in farm production or in some other gainful employment?"

The same sort of question applies to running a roadside stand or selling on a local farmer's market. Such marketing activities are, in effect, supplementary enterprises. And the question is whether this kind of diversification will pay better than specializing in farm production and selling to a wholesale assembler or other specialized marketing firm.

There is no general answer to this question; each case must be judged on its own merits. But some observations may be made regarding the likelihood that diversifying into marketing will pay.

When Is Retail Selling by Producers Profitable?

Profitable opportunities for a farmer to retail his own products are most likely if he produces commodities that can be

---

[1] Actually, the owner of an orange grove may contract for the pruning, spraying, and other production operations along with the harvesting. But he then becomes more of a special type of landlord than an operating farmer.

sold to the consumer with little or no processing or other handling. Fresh produce, dairy and poultry products are most clearly in this category. The wheat farmer is not likely to find it profitable to mill his wheat into flour, much less to bake it into bread. Milling and baking are complex businesses, requiring special skills and costly equipment to be done on an efficient scale. They are unlikely supplementary enterprises to running a farm.[2]

Again, profitable opportunities for farmer retailing are pretty much limited to farmers living close to towns or cities that offer a retail market. Otherwise, time and transportation costs are likely to be too great relative to the volume that an individual farmer has to sell.[3] Profitable operation of a roadside stand requires location on a heavily traveled (and not too high-speed) highway.

Personal considerations likewise enter in. An old Chinese proverb says, "Do not open a shop unless you like to smile." Success in selling one's farm products at retail may depend upon one's ability to build up a clientele of loyal customers. Unless one is an efficient salesman, the returns are not likely to be worth the costs.

A farmer may be able to build up a profitable trade in specialty items like winter squash and pumpkins, or special varieties of fruits and vegetables that are locally favored, which mass distributors consider unprofitable because of the small volume of sales; and likewise, products like the soft fruits or sweet corn, that are hard to get to the consumer at their highest quality through the usual commercial channels. Here the high price that particular customers will pay to get products they want may give the farmer a good return on his capital and labor applied to marketing.

Maintaining steady customers is easiest if one has something to sell all year round, or at least during a long season. This also permits making fullest use of special facilities and equip-

---

[2] Farm wives who sell baked goods on farm women's markets do not usually bake them out of flour ground from wheat grown on their own farms.

[3] Some fruit growers, as an exception, do a mail-order business, shipping by parcel post or express. Usually they cater to an elite trade and feature special quality and fancy holiday packs.

ment—a consideration from the cost standpoint. Eggs and dairy products, which can be produced all year, best fit this specification. In the case of truck crops, storable products like apples and potatoes help prolong the season.

The advantage of a year-round business, plus cost savings associated with larger volume of sales, may lead a farmer not merely to sell his own produce, but also to buy from neighbors or even to buy produce through commercial wholesale channels. If purchased products become an important share of his business, the question arises whether marketing is any longer just a supplement to his farming operations. He may then need to ask himself whether it is worth his while to continue farming or whether he might make more by giving up farm production and specializing wholly in marketing.

The Basic Question—Which Way Pays Best?

We have discussed in some detail things that a farmer should consider in deciding whether there is a profitable opportunity to undertake direct retailing of his products. (Some of the same considerations would apply to selling directly to local retail stores.) In economic terms, to do this means performing certain marketing services that are most often performed by specialized marketing firms. He hopes to get paid for these services in the form of a higher price for his product. But it will cost him something to perform the services. His problem, therefore, is to estimate whether performing them offers a better return over costs than he could get through alternative uses of his time, energy, and money investment.

The same question applies, in greater or lesser degree, to other choices open to a farmer regarding when, where, and in what form to market his products. Marketing involves him in certain costs—greater or less, depending on whether he performs many marketing services or few. Hence, he must compare these costs with his expected returns from different outlets. Historically, certainly, the trend has been for farmers to specialize in production and for processing and marketing to be performed increasingly by firms specializing in these activities.

Later chapters will present some of the economic principles applicable in choosing among alternative methods of marketing that may be open to farmers. They will discuss, on the one hand, the cost side of the picture, and principles useful in analyzing costs. And they will discuss the demand side—the principles useful in deciding when, where, and in what form to sell to get the greatest net return and to avoid unnecessary risks.

QUESTIONS FOR DISCUSSION

1. What is the line of separation between the production and marketing of farm products?

2. Is a farmer better off if he can sell to the consumer direct without the middleman? Explain.

3. Do you expect a decline or an increase in farm sales made direct to consumers? Give reasons.

4. Why do farmers and consumers often criticize middlemen? Do you think that the usual criticisms are justified—in whole or in part? Explain.

SUPPLEMENTARY READING

1. Kohls, R. L., *Marketing of Agricultural Products*. New York: The Macmillan Company, 1955, Ch. 2.
2. Norton and Scranton, *Marketing Farm Products*. Danville, Ill.: The Interstate, 1949, Chs. 2 and 14.
3. Waugh, Frederick V., *Readings on Agricultural Marketing*. Ames: Iowa State College Press, 1954, pp. 10-17. This includes excerpts from the writings of George Washington, John Cassels, Margaret Reid, Clark and Weld, and Edwin G. Nourse.

4

Policies of
Marketing Firms

Many different types of firms participate in the marketing of farm products. Some, like wholesale shippers and receivers, elevator operators, canners, flour millers, meat packers, grocery stores, and restaurants, specialize in handling farm products, or even one particular product. Others, like railways and truck lines, telephone and telegraph companies, banks and fire insurance companies, advertising agencies and media, and department stores, specialize in performing a particular function which they may perform in many other connections besides the marketing of farm products. Railroads transport all kinds of goods, although hauling farm products is a very important part of the business of many of them, just as loans to companies engaged in the marketing of farm products is an important part of the business of many commercial banks.

We shall focus most of our attention on firms of the first type. We shall also be concerned most often with firms that chiefly handle raw farm products or those processed products made mainly from them—with canners and bakers more often than with automobile manufacturers.

The chief agricultural consumers' goods—food, clothing, and tobacco products—together account for some 40 per cent of all consumer expenditure in the United States. The processors and distributors that get these products from farm to consumer include several of the nation's largest corporations (such as Swift and Company, General Foods, and Safeway Stores).

They also include a vast number of smaller firms—nearly half a million food retailers alone, although their number is declining rapidly. Each of these firms must continuously be making short-range and long-range decisions regarding its operations. How much money the firm makes—and how well it fulfills its function from society's standpoint—will depend upon how wisely it makes these decisions.

A look at a few types of marketing firms to see how they operate and what sorts of decisions they must make will show that typically they face the same kinds of problems that face the farmer in the market: *when* to buy and when to sell; *where* to buy and where to sell; *what* products to buy and sell, and *in what form*. And always there are the problems of *costs*—how to keep them to a minimum; and *risks*—how to avoid them, or what allowance to make for those that cannot be avoided.

There are thousands of individuals and firms handling agricultural produce after it leaves the farm. Theirs is the job of packing, grading, cleaning, processing, transporting, and distributing.

The economic motive for these individuals and firms is to receive returns for their labor or investment comparable with returns they could get in some other job or enterprise. The incentives for firms handling farm produce is to maximize profit by either minimizing costs or increasing the revenues from sales. It is important, therefore, to understand the amount of competition between firms and between farmers and handlers.

Some Typical Firms

A MILK DEALER

Preparing milk for consumption starts when the milk is placed in the cooler or farm tank on the farm. The milk is then delivered to a plant by truckers who maintain a pickup route making regular calls at each farm. The trucking expense is generally paid by the producer and the operation is under the supervision of the dealer. Failure to pick up milk at any time would result in spoilage at the farm and shortages at the plant.

If assembled in cans, the milk is received at the plant in a receiving room, where it is examined for quality. Then the milk is poured into a weighing tank, where it is weighed and where a daily record is kept of amounts received from each farm. Samples of each producer's milk are taken for laboratory testing to determine the butterfat content. This will be done at the farm if milk is assembled in bulk tanks.

After sampling, various grades are segregated and those which require special handling are weighed separately and routed through special channels in the plant. From the weighing tank the milk is piped to the pasteurizing vats or to refrigerated holding tanks. The storage tanks are necessary to take care of day-to-day fluctuations in supply and demand, particularly on weekends and holidays.

Pasteurizing by the "holding" method means heating the milk to 143 degrees for thirty minutes. After pasteurization, the milk is cooled by running over refrigerated coolers and is then piped to the bottle filler and capper. From the capper the operator transfers the milk to cases, which are then put into the refrigerator storage chest to await delivery.

A small city plant would require a crew of at least six men. It would process approximately 5,000 quarts a day and would need an office staff of three girls and a manager to keep records and operate the business. The capital investment in equipment would be about $30 per quart of volume hauled. The distribution service would require at least eleven men and eight trucks. On the retail routes, each driver serves about 300 customers. To provide for days off, holidays, vacations, and sickness, it would be necessary to have three spare men.

As the size of plant increases, there will be a similar increase in the number of men employed and the pieces of equipment and delivery trucks required. The manager must buy supplies and equipment and hire labor at rates comparable with those paid for work in the vicinity. If located in an industrial area, the wages paid dairy plant operators and delivery men must be as attractive as those paid by other industries in that location.

BROILER PROCESSING

A broiler dressing plant with a capacity of 1,200 broilers per hour would require 53 men in the plant and 5 office and supervisory staff.[1] The birds are received in the plant. A workman takes the birds from the crates and hangs them by one foot on a shackle which is suspended from the ceiling, for killing and bleeding. The birds are then scalded, moved back and forth in the water, removed from the shackles, and placed in a power drum picker, where pin feathers are removed. The finished birds are transferred to a board where they are dressed, then eviscerated and cut up. After this they are sized, cooled, and packaged ready for shipment.

The plant investment would be $138,000, of which $36,000 would be for building, $87,000 for equipment, and the rest for land, refrigeration, and well. This would amount to $1.67 per pound of broiler capacity. The major job is eviscerating, which takes 25 of the 53 plant laborers employed. One employee can eviscerate 48 birds per hour and another can cool, size, and package 133 birds per hour.

With a plant of this size, it is possible to set up an assembly-line operation to keep the birds moving, prevent bottlenecks, and make effective use of equipment and labor. There are undoubtedly economies of scale possible with further increases in the size of the operation. Efficiency of operation is dependent on a steady supply of birds, a standardized form for sale, and a low rate of labor turnover.

The job of management is one of supervision and organization of the numerous operations. Trade contacts must be maintained for sales and supplies, and frequently the poultry buyer must take a managerial role to keep the plant operating at capacity.

PACKAGING PEARS

The fresh pear market requires a well-packed, evenly graded fruit that can be hauled with a minimum of damage. Plants

---

[1] G. B. Rogers and E. T. Bardwell, *Marketing New England Poultry. 2. Economies of Scale in Chicken Processing.* Station Bulletin 459, University of New Hampshire Agricultural Experiment Station, 1959.

After thorough cooling, eviscerated chickens are removed from chill tanks and placed on drainage line. Drainage takes about 12 minutes.

of a firm preparing fruit for market consist of buildings, equipment, and land. There are nine stages of operation in a typical pear-packing plant. These are dumping, grading, packing, stamping, lidding, car and truck loading, box making, labeling empty packing box and material supply, and packaging cannery and cull fruit.[2]

The general costs for a standard box equivalent (48 pounds) would be approximately as follows: direct labor, 39 cents; materials, 51 cents; and fixed costs, 10 cents. The high proportion of costs in the category of labor requires that maximum use be made of time and space during the working day. The assembly lines for grading and packing and remaining stages must receive a steady supply of produce through the working

[2] French, Sammet, and Bressler, "Economic Efficiency in Plant Operations with Special Reference to the Marketing of California Pears," *Hilgardia*. University of California, Vol. 24, No. 19, July, 1956, p. 601.

day. Similar operations and problems exist for packing plants for other fruits and vegetables.

A tomato-packing plant will receive thousands of green field tomatoes each day during the season. Shipped under refrigeration, they are moved into temperature- and humidity-controlled ripening rooms until ready for final processing. They are then washed, inspected, and graded before being packaged and shipped.

Courtesy U.S.D.A.

As fruit moves along conveyor belt, women sorters remove off-colored and other-wise defective fruit.

SOYBEAN PROCESSING

Soybeans are hauled from the farms or shipped by rail to processing plants, where the beans are cleaned and put through rollers to crack and flake them. They then go to cookers or driers, and in the process the oil is pressed out or chemically extracted. The remaining hulls and flakes are put through grinders and processed into feed. The oil and the feed supplements are then shipped to distributors or to oil refineries for further processing and subsequent sale.

The Industry, the Firm, and the Plant

An industry is composed of firms and plants. A firm can be identified as a management unit where all major decisions or operations are centralized in one man or group of men who own or manage the capital resources involved. A plant can be referred to as an operational unit of the firm. The plant manager controls the physical production operation in relation to plant costs, but major market and policy decisions will be made at the firm level. A firm may have several plants or only one plant. With several plants, the operations may be complementary. For example, a firm may have an ice-cream plant, a whole-milk plant, and a dried-milk plant, all using the same raw material. A firm may handle fresh fruit and processed fruit, with different plants handling and packing fresh fruit and freezing or otherwise processing the fruit.

With only one plant, the management decisions are somewhat simplified, but there are limits to diversification and cost reductions by single plants which may be available to firms with more than one plant.

The soybean-processing industry, for example, has 140 processing plants in the United States, but this does not mean that there are 140 firms. The dairy industry is composed of many firms, some of which have processing plants in several states. Management decisions are centralized but operational decisions are more localized. The same is true for meat-packing firms, grain handlers, millers, cotton gins, fruit packers, and so on.

There were 40,000 establishments in 1947 manufacturing food and kindred products in the United States all under various management and plant-firm arrangements.

Marketing Policies

For purposes of economic analysis, it is possible to discuss marketing policies at the industry level, at the firm level, and at the plant level of operation while still appreciating their interrelationship. The milling industry, for example, has certain problems of grain production, transportation, location, and consumer preferences that are peculiar to it. Its over-all

Courtesy U.S.D.A.

Trucks await their turn to unload rough rice at a drying plant.

policy is concerned with the production of wheat, the response of farmers to government price supports, or the effect of reciprocal trade agreements on the demand for its products and on the raw material from which its products are made. It is concerned with the level of employment, railway rate increases, and competition on the international market.

The cotton industry has similar problems which can best be solved at the industry level, such as the competition of nylon, tariffs on imported cotton, world production, and the supply response of domestic cotton farmers to changes in price.

The dairy industry faces changes in the demand for milk and milk products. Industry-wide advertising schemes and promotions are evidence of this. The number of cows and production per cow are of primary concern to the industry, as is the increased production of competing foods.

The ownership of a firm may be by one person, a corporation, or a group of persons. Associations of firms frequently meet and discuss industry problems and agree on a general policy for their own economic betterment. Unless there are only a few firms in an industry, the exchange of ideas and formation of industry policy does not interfere with the competition between firms or with those problems that are peculiar to each firm.

In a competitive society it is the objective of owners of a firm to maximize returns on their capital investments. The health of a firm is frequently measured by the dividends it pays the stockholders or by the market price of its stocks. If owned and operated by an individual and his family, its success is measured by profit, employee relations, and the firm's dynamics of growth.

The owners, or the management on behalf of the owners, must follow certain principles of economic behavior if they are to remain in business. Their business may be trucking, processing, distributing, wholesaling, or retailing, but in all cases they must continually strive for the least cost combination of inputs. By "inputs" is meant labor, supplies, rent, machinery, oil, electricity, and so on. In this way the average cost per unit of product will be as low as possible at any particular time. The price level will depend on the competition between firms and on demand for the product, and a lower average cost means greater returns per dollar spent than a higher average cost for the same product.

The management of a firm requires talent for the organization of factors of production, adequate capital reserves for necessary changes, and an appreciation of the long-run competitive position. Such a job will require the seeking out of low-cost supplies, the substitution of one plan for another, the expansion or maintenance of markets, knowledge of new technological developments, and continuous attempts at cost reduction.

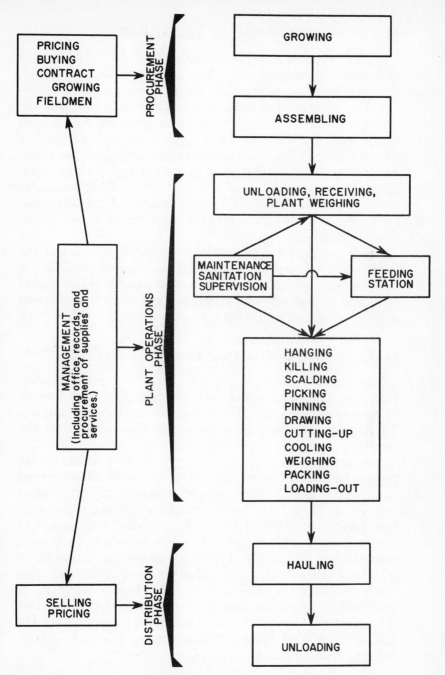

Functions Carried Out by Poultry-Processing Firms. (From *University of New Hampshire Agricultural Experiment Station Bulletin 459.*)

41

Such enterprises as we have indicated can be further broken down into operational units. The plant may be one. Within the plant there are also various stages of the production process. The processing of milk in our illustration included the stages of delivery from farm to plant, weighing and recording, testing, pasteurizing, bottling, and distributing. Poultry dressing follows the steps of taking the birds from the crate, hanging, scalding, feathering, eviscerating, and packing. Similar stages of operation are followed for packing pears. By analysis of each stage and by co-ordination of the labor and equipment used at each stage, the achievement of cost reduction is simplified.

These are the jobs of plant managers, and the cost of the final product is dependent on their decisions and on the efficiency with which these are carried out by thousands of firms and individuals who determine the speed and the cost of processing and marketing agricultural produce.

Marketing Policies of the Final Users of Farm Products

The types of firms described in the preceding section provide the channels through which farm products flow from farmers to consumers and move the products through these channels. To complete the picture, there remain the end-users of the products.

The greatest number of end-users of farm products are private families or households. These are most often referred to as "consumers." They include, however, a considerable number of "institutional" users: hospitals, schools, clubs, military establishments, and homes for orphans, the aged, and the indigent—a wide variety of public agencies and private organizations that feed and often clothe groups of people. In addition to these are various industries using agricultural raw materials that we arbitrarily class as end-users rather than as intermediate processors because the farm products used lose their identity or are relatively unimportant components of the end products that such industries make. (The automobile industry was previously given as an example.)

Quantity Buying

Large-volume users such as institutions or industrial users are likely to do a more highly specialized and systematic job of buying farm products than most family households. They commonly use larger quantities. They need to plan their buying well in advance. For products that are storable, they may keep substantial inventories on hand. For perishables, they need to have established sources of supply that they can depend upon continuously. Often they employ specialized buyers, who may, for example, belong to the National Association of Purchasing Agents, an organization that furnishes technical and economic services to professional buyers or the firms and institutions they represent.

Large institutional and industrial users of farm products find that it pays them to follow careful buying practices. Studying price trends, supply-and-demand relationships, and other market information as a guide to selection and timing of purchases may result in substantial savings. Shopping around, or contracting with suppliers on the basis of competitive bids, may bring appreciable price advantages. Sellers will often figure prices closely in order to get the large orders of such buyers. Sellers may likewise be willing to go to extra efforts to furnish particular qualities desired, or to put products up in special packs, or to provide other special services to meet such buyer's specifications.

The marketing problems of institutional and industrial users can, again, be classified under the headings: *where* to buy and *when* to buy, *what* to buy, and *in what form*. On the latter point they may have additional flexibility of choice as between raw products, semi-manufactured, and finished goods. As large users, it may pay them to do some of their own processing—canning or baking, for example, or operating their own mill. It may also pay them to haul some products in their own trucks and store them in their own warehouses. In each case, however, they will need to compare the *costs* of performing such services for themselves with the resulting savings in price on their purchases. And they will have to

Courtesy U.S.D.A.

A Shopper Making a Choice in the Vegetable and Fresh Fruit Department of a Supermarket.

allow for *risks* of spoilage, damage, or deterioration of products in their hands, as well as for the usual market risks of unforeseen price fluctuations.

Buying for the Home

Household users of farm products typically are less systematic buyers of farm products. Many housewives do, of course, study advertisements carefully and shop around to get the best bargains. But in the nature of things, they can hardly be specialists or market analysts in all the wide variety of products that they buy. Nor can they spend all their time at this task. They have other things to do. Most of them have limited storage facilities to permit buying products ahead, and limited time or facilities to permit extensive home processing.

Household users buy predominantly from hand to mouth, and are willing to pay for ready-made, ready-mixed, precooked products. They are likely to do most of their buying at one or a few stores whose prices and services they find satisfactory. And, while some may be quite flexible in their purchases, depending upon what "looks good" in the store, this necessarily reflects more the quick judgment of the moment—what the merchandisers call "impulse buying"—than a considered judgment based upon thorough analysis of the market.

This does not mean that most housewives are "inefficient" buyers of farm products. It means only that typically they buy so frequently such small quantities of so many different things that they must depend heavily upon familiar stores, familiar products, and familiar brands, and upon quick, on-the-spot selection. For most of them, the *costs* of doing otherwise, in terms of time and energy, would outweigh the savings.

A consequence of this is that both retail distributors and processors of branded products depend heavily upon sales efforts for building "customer loyalty" to their stores or their brands by trading on the housewives' need to buy by habit. And they depend heavily upon attention-getting devices—striking advertisements, dramatic price reductions or two-for-the-price-of-one tie-ins of a few "leaders," fancy displays and packaging, give-away stamps or door prizes, and the like—in order to attract new customers. Most of them cater to the "mass market." That is to say, special products or qualities, special packs, or other special services for individual household buyers are too costly in relation to the small size of purchases, so the sellers try to devise products and services that they hope will appeal to the mass of consumers, and then try through heavy "promotion" to persuade as many consumers as possible to buy these products.

Household buyers of farm products face the same basic problems as do institutional or industrial buyers: *where* and *when* to buy, *what* products, and *in what forms*. But lack of time—a major *cost* factor—limits their choices of "where," and the necessity of buying hand-to-mouth limits their choices of "when." And while an enormous variety of products and forms of products are continually urged upon them by the sellers, again limitations of time and energy, plus lack of comparative information, restricts most of them most of the time to the familiar routine, except as snap judgment or impulse leads them to experiment. These characteristics of retail trade have consequences, both on the buying and on the selling side, that we shall need to give particular attention to later on.

QUESTIONS FOR DISCUSSION

1. Define a "marketing firm."
2. Give several examples of economic decisions that must be made by typical marketing firms.
3. Will it benefit a marketing firm to pay as low a price as possible to producers for their produce? If not, why not?
4. Are the aims of an industry (the dairy industry, for example) the same as the aims of the individual firms, or individual persons, making up the industry? If not, explain how, and why, the aims differ.

SUPPLEMENTARY READING

1. Brunk, Max E., and L. B. Darrah, *Marketing of Agricultural Products.* New York: Ronald Press Company, 1955, Chs. 20 and 21.
2. Vaile, R. S., E. T. Grether, and R. Cor, *Marketing in the American Economy.* New York: Ronald Press Company, 1952, Chs. 2 and 4.
3. *Marketing: Yearbook of Agriculture, 1954.* Washington, D.C.: U. S. Department of Agriculture, pp. 22-75.

5

Marketing Systems
and the Role of Price

We have taken a rapid look at the different types of firms and of people—farmers, intermediate handlers, processors, and distributors, industrial and institutional users, and private households—that are involved in the marketing of agricultural commodities. Each of them buys or sells or both buys and sells. Each of them faces decisions on what to buy or sell, in what form, where, and when. Each faces various costs associated with his marketing activities, which he seeks to keep to a minimum in relation to the returns or benefits that he gets. Each must plan his operations, and in doing so must forecast his needs and opportunities and run risks that things may not turn out as planned.

Each of these participants in the marketing process is a free agent, in that he makes his own choices and decisions in the light of his own desires, knowledge, and judgment. Yet something must tie together this multiplicity of independent daily decisions. If all farmers, exercising their freedom of choice, decided to produce only wheat, or if all consumers decided to eat only oranges, or if all shippers decided to ship only to Chicago, the result would be chaos rather than an orderly marketing system.

What is it that assures us against such breakdowns, against the possibility that large numbers of participants in marketing will suddenly choose to do things contrary to the orderly and reliable operation of the market? The answer is not the same in all countries. In Russia, and in other dictatorships, the government exercises far-reaching controls over prices, production,

47

and marketing. In the United States, we rely mainly upon competition—whereby each person sells to maximize his own profit. But, even in the United States, World War II necessitated a War Food Administration and an Office of Price Administration. And even in peace times, we have many regulations—for example, the Interstate Commerce Commission railroad and truck regulations and the United States Department of Agriculture regulations dealing with milk prices and vegetable shipments under marketing agreements and orders.

Stability Because of Custom

Perhaps the most fundamental protection against breakdowns of the marketing system is the continuity of custom. By and large, most of the participants most of the time continue to do the same sorts of things they have been doing. Through training and experience they have developed certain patterns of behavior—working at certain types of jobs by which they have learned to make a living, and using certain types of foods and clothing that they have learned to prefer as consumers. For the most part, they continue in these customary patterns.

These patterns of behavior are reinforced by a vast network of established relationships among the participants, upon which they have all come to rely. The farmer has confidence not only that a market will exist for his products in the season ahead, but that outlets he has sold through before or adequate substitutes will still be there. The housewife has confidence that the stores from which she is accustomed to buying will still be operating next week and will still offer the variety of merchandise she has come to depend upon for her basic shopping needs. And all the intermediaries between have their established trade connections in established markets at which they are accustomed to deal and their established sources of finance and of market information. They are confident that these will continue.

Stability Because of Capital Investment

The large amount of investment in specialized facilities and equipment is another stabilizing factor in agricultural marketing. The dairy farmer, with his herd and his barns and his milking equipment, cannot afford capriciously just to quit dairying. He continues to operate until he can sell out at a price that will, if possible, at least recover his capital investment. Similarly with the owners of a creamery, a canning plant, a warehouse, or a supermarket. And even when such facilities are sold, they do not usually go out of operation. The new owners continue to operate them so long as there is any possibility of making money in the kind of business for which they are uniquely designed and equipped.

We are so used to this continuity of customary practices, arrangements, and facilities by which marketing is carried on, and the legal and institutional framework that supports it, that we largely take them for granted. One can imagine a changeless economy in which this is all that would be necessary to maintain the system in operation. Individuals and business firms would continue in their daily and yearly patterns of activity, and the system would carry on of its own momentum.

Allowing for Change

But ours is not a changeless economy. Population growth means a continuously increasing number of mouths to feed and backs to clothe. Wars and other catastrophes cause great upheavals in the economy. Technological progress recurrently provides new processes and new products. As a people, we have become accustomed not to sameness, but to a continuously rising level of living, in terms of agricultural products as well as other goods. And agricultural production, particularly, is subject to vicissitudes of weather and other biological hazards that cause substantial fluctuations from time to time in what is produced for market. Thus, people cannot depend merely upon following the past in their marketing decisions. They face continuously changing conditions, and their choices must be altered correspondingly. What, then, co-ordinates the marketing decisions of free individuals in a changing economy?

The Role of Competitive Prices

In our type of economy, we depend chiefly upon competitive prices to fill this need. (All economies rely upon prices. In some cases, the prices are set by government agencies. Traditionally, farm-product prices in the United States have been "free"—that is, they have been set by the impersonal forces of demand and supply, operating in competitive markets.) The preceding chapters emphasized repeatedly that the marketing decisions of all the different types of participants in agricultural marketing revolve around the basic problems *what* to buy or sell, in what *form, when,* and *where;* and that, in making these decisions, they must take account of associated *costs* and must allow for associated *risks.* In all of these decisions, expected *prices* are a chief guide.

Sellers want to net the most money they can for their products and services. Buyers want to get the most goods and services for their money. How much money sellers get depends upon the *prices* at which they sell. How much buyers get for their money depends upon the *prices* at which they buy. Buyers and sellers, therefore, both make their decisions on the basis of prices—present prices or anticipated future prices.

Their cost calculations, likewise, are largely in terms of prices: wage rates, freight rates, interest rates, or, in the case of their own efforts, the rate of pay or other return that they might get from some different use of their time and energy—what we shall refer to as "opportunity costs." (Housewives are an exception, in that most of them do not actually calculate a money value for their services. Yet they do, in effect, make some such evaluation whenever they decide whether it is worth the time to shop additional stores. And a money comparison is clearly implied when a housewife decides whether to take a job for pay.)

Similarly with respect to risks, marketing plans for the future are based on anticipated prices. The major risks involved arise from the possible incorrectness of these anticipations. Whether the turkey grower makes or loses money for the year depends upon how well he guesses, at spring breeding time, what the fall price of turkeys will be in relation to prices of feed and other cost items, and in relation to prices of other things that he might produce instead. Large meat packers have lost millions of dollars on occasion through storing a large quantity of pork in the winter, in anticipation that the next summer's price would be high, and having it turn out low instead—*or* by putting only a little pork into storage in the winter and having the next summer's price turn out high.

Prices, Past and Anticipated

A few pages earlier, it was said that the continuity of custom is the most fundamental factor in co-ordinating the independent decisions of the people and the firms engaged in agricultural marketing. Here it is asserted that prices are what determine these decisions. This may seem to be a contradiction.

To resolve this paradox requires a further examination of how decisions are made. Let us consider budget-making. A farmer, a meat packer, a retailer, or a housewife, in drawing up a budget for the year, does not start with a blank sheet of paper. He or she first puts down last year's income and expenses—perhaps the figures for the last several years. These figures are then adjusted in the light of changes that are known or anticipated, in order to get estimates for this year. Prices are a main factor in making these adjustments. But the price information itself is ordinarily related to the past. Published market forecasts are typically put in terms of expected changes: this year's prices will average so much higher for this item, and so much lower for that item, than last year's. Similarly with other kinds of financial data. The annual report of a corporation typically compares this year's operating results with those of last year, or of the last several years. Published business statistics ordinarily give comparisons of this month or this week with last month or last week, and with the corresponding week a year ago. Even daily market reports look backward for a basis of comparison: hogs up 50 cents from yesterday; steers down 75 cents.

Typically, marketing decisions start from the past, the "continuity of custom." This is the part, as previously indicated, that we take for granted. Past patterns are then adjusted in the light of present and prospective changes in prices and other conditions. This is the part that we are conscious of in decision-making, the part that is "important" in the sense that we are under pressure to do something about it. It is the area in which we have choices open to us, and the area in which those choices are determined, for better of for worse.

Prices, then, or price changes, are main guides to *changes* in patterns of market behavior—to adjustments to changing conditions, to progress over time. But, what claim do they have as effective and desirable *co-ordinators of marketing decisions?* How can they make the system hang together in an orderly fashion?

Co-ordination of Firms' Activities

No one firm can operate in complete isolation from other firms. The final product of one firm is the raw material for another firm. If two firms are processing the same product, then they will meet on the buyers' market and on the sellers' market, and the behavior of one firm as to price and market policy will influence the practices of the other firm.

Competition is one way of co-ordinating economic activities. This co-ordination will be at the world, national, or regional level, depending on the extent of trade. For example, the prices paid by Firm A in New York State will have a more direct influence on the prices offered by Firm B in New York State than they will on Firm C buying in California or Texas. On the other hand, if a product can be readily shipped from California to New York, then the prices paid in both those regions must bear a close relationship. An eastern firm buying hogs in Iowa will compete with a Pacific Coast firm buying the same product. The price of hogs in Iowa will reflect the demand in the east and on the Pacific Coast as well as local supply conditions.

Thus, competitive pricing is the main way of allocating supplies of food among consumers in democracies. If supplies are short and demand strong, then prices tend to rise and additional supplies will be attracted to that market. If supplies are heavy and demand light, prices decline, tending to reduce production or to divert available supplies to higher-price markets. But democracies do not rely wholly upon competition, as we shall see in Part 4.

Price Defines the Market

The market for a product includes all potential buyers and sellers (or all the forces of demand and supply) at a given place and time. The market price is formed by the forces that act throughout a market area, which may be very large, such as the world-wide wheat market, or very small, such as the market for cord wood in Amherst, Massachusetts. Each product has one or more points of sale. These may be at the farm, the terminal market, the processing plant, or the retail store. There is a relationship between prices at each point of sale. The farm price is the price received by farmers from a processor. The processor in turn uses this price plus his costs of operation to arrive at a selling price. This price is the buying price for a retailer, who will use this as a base for calculating his selling price.

The simple concept of a market as a place where goods change hands or where produce is sold by a farmer to a consumer is quite inadequate for describing the series of transactions which occur for the majority of agricultural products.

The retail market, the wholesale market, the jobbers' market, the dealers' market, and the farm market are all types of markets. The "market" for a seller is at the transfer of title. The "market" for a product consists of all the points in the movement from producer to consumer at which price is established and the product changes hands. If a consumer buys strawberries for his own use from a farmer, this transaction establishes the market price for strawberries at that particular time and place. If, however, the strawberries are bought by a dealer, sold to a processor, then a wholesaler, and then to a retailer where they are finally bought by a consumer, the "market" for strawberries must include all of these transactions.

Same Price for Same Product

Where there is competition between firms buying and selling farm produce, there is a tendency for the same price to be paid for the same product in all markets. Firms handling the same product study one another's behavior and in many cases establish certain ethics of competition by means of associations or other trade groups. This does not necessarily reduce competition but rather prevents "cutthroat" competition, which disrupts markets to the ultimate detriment of all concerned.

Each agricultural commodity is bought and sold by groups of specialized firms which together make up the marketing system. These firms may be processors located in producing areas or wholesalers located in consuming areas, but the prices they pay are co-ordinated by a *pricing system* that reflects total supply and total demand for every commodity.

QUESTIONS FOR DISCUSSION

1. In a purely competitive economy, prices would be "free," and would allocate production and consumption. In Russia, the government fixes prices. During World War II, the United States Government fixed prices. Do fixed prices affect production and consumption? What problems must a government meet if it fixes prices?

2. What about prices that are "administered" by large corporations, or are influenced by trade associations, by farmers' cooperatives, by labor unions, or by government programs?

3. Are unexpected changes in demand and price a cost to the marketing firm?

SUPPLEMENTARY READING

1. Bober, M. M., *Intermediate Price and Income Theory.* New York: W. W. Norton Company, Inc., 1955, Ch. 1.
2. Stigler, G. J., *The Theory of Price.* New York: The Macmillan Company, 1947, Ch. 3.
3. Vaile, R. S., *et al., Marketing in the American Economy.* New York: Ronald Press Company, 1952, Ch. 23.

6

The Perfect Market

Many economists have been intrigued with the concept of a perfect market—meaning a market governed by perfect competition.[1] In such a market, the price of any commodity would equal the marginal cost of producing and marketing it. Geographical price differentials would equal differences in freight rates and similar costs. Price differentials through time would equal differences in storage and similar costs associated with time. Price differences for different forms of a commodity (fresh oranges, canned orange juice, and frozen concentrate, for example) would equal differences in costs of producing and marketing them.

Moreover, wages for a given grade of labor would be the same in all occupations. And profits would be the same in all industries. A dollar invested in agriculture would return the same as a dollar invested in copper mining, railroads, or steel.

This concept of a perfect market is commonly used for either of two purposes: first, to explain existing markets; second, to indicate what is "desirable," or "beneficial," or even "optimal," in some sense.

Without question, the concept of a perfect market helps to explain many real agricultural markets. Take milk, for example. Several studies [2] have shown that geographical varia-

---

[1] A good detailed discussion of this concept can be found in Geoffrey S. Shepherd, *Marketing Farm Products*. Ames: Iowa State College Press, 1946, pp. 399-409.

[2] Raymond G. Bressler *et al.*, several bulletins of the Connecticut Agr. Exp. Station in the late 1930's and in the 1940's; William Bredo and Anthony S. Rojko, "Prices and Milksheds of Northeastern Markets," *Northeastern Regional Publication* No. 9, Univ. of Mass., Agr. Exp. Sta. Bull. No. 470, 1952; "Regulations Affecting the Movement and Merchandising of Milk," *Marketing Research Report* No. 98, Agricultural Marketing Service, 1955, pp. 87-100.

tions in fluid-milk prices are very nearly those that would occur in a perfect market. This suggests, at least, that competition is still the dominant force in fluid-milk marketing, even though we all know that there are many departures from perfection.

The concept of a perfect market helps to explain not only what actually happens in milk marketing, but it helps explain other commodity markets, both national and international. The markets for grain, cotton, hogs, and potatoes are rather closely in line with what we would expect under perfect competition. Of course, there are departures, and the departures are worthy of study. The important point here is that there is a high degree of correspondence between the actual market prices of many farm products and those that would exist under perfect competition.

But what about the other common use of the concept: to indicate what is desirable, beneficial, optimal? Many economists seem to believe that the perfect market would be optimal—that it would maximize the well-being of the public as a whole. This is, of course, a value judgment. Don't accept it uncritically, nor without important reservations. Especially, don't jump to the conclusion that everything would be satisfactory if all governmental programs were dropped.

Consider the general argument that a perfect market would be optimal. Of course, perfection sounds like a good thing. But why perfectly competitive, rather than perfectly monopolistic, for example? Those few persons who have tried to *prove* that a perfect market is optimal are careful to define it as a market in which each unit of each good sells at its marginal cost. If the price of potatoes were higher than the marginal cost of producing and marketing them, output would be increased, the price would fall, marginal costs would increase, and the two would come to balance. This is exactly what would happen under perfect competition. Why is this sometimes said to be best, or optimal?

Many of the champions of a perfect market have never really tried to prove that it is best. Rather, they remember vaguely some of the ideas perpetrated by the classical economists. That good old Scotchman, Adam Smith, advanced an interesting defense of the notion back in 1776—the year of independence for the United States. Smith's central argument [3] was:

> The produce of industry is what it adds to the subject or materials upon which it is employed. In proportion as the value of this produce is great or small, so will likewise be the profits of the employer. But it is only for the sake of profit that any man employs a capital in the support of industry; and he will always, therefore, endeavor to employ it in the support of that industry of which the produce is likely to be of the greatest value, or to exchange for the greatest quantity either of money or of other goods.
>
> But the annual revenue of every society is always precisely equal to the exchangeable value of the whole annual produce of its industry, or rather is precisely the same thing with that exchangeable value. As every individual, therefore, endeavors as much as he can both to employ his capital in the support of domestic industry, and so to direct that industry that its produce may be of the greatest value; every individual necessarily labours to render the annual revenue of the society as great as he can. He generally, indeed neither intends to promote the public interest, nor knows how much he is promoting it. By preferring the support of domestic to that of foreign industry, he intends only his own security; and by directing that industry in such a manner as its produce may be of greatest value, he intends only his own gain, and he is in this, as in many other cases, led by an invisible hand to promote an end which was no part of his intention. Nor is it always the worse for society that it was no part of it. By pursuing his own interest he frequently promotes that of society more effectually than when he really intends to promote it. I have never known much good done by those who affected to trade for the public good. It is an affectation, indeed, not very common among merchants, and very few words need be employed in dissuading them from it.

We have quoted Smith at some length, because he is eloquent, persuasive, understandable. The student wanting more

---

[3] Taken from Adam Smith, *An Inquiry into the Nature and Causes of the Wealth of Nations.* New York: Modern Library, 1937, p. 423.

elaborate analysis should consult Pigou [4] or Samuelson.[5]

Shall we accept Smith's argument, with or without reservations?

A recent skeptic,[6] after discussing the problems of unstable farm prices and incomes, states:

> But a widely held myth blankets public awareness of these problems, and beclouds the issues involved. It is the myth of an automatically adjusting agriculture—an agriculture that tends toward a golden mean. . . . in each peacetime slump, the view is expressed over and over again to this effect: "Agriculture is basically sound; it is just a little out of balance. And if we wait a little while for the necessary adjustments to take place, or pass some emergency legislation to help the necessary adjustments to take place, all will be well." This is the myth of a self-adjusting, or easily adjusted, agriculture.

Is the invisible hand a reality or a myth? Is the perfect market good, bad, or indifferent? We shall not give doctrinaire answers. You should think for yourself. But we would advise you not to swallow the perfect market without several grains of salt. And when you read learned writings about the optimum use of resources, don't jump too quickly to the conclusion that this is necessarily the same thing as the use of resources we would get under perfect competition.

Just a few points to consider are these:

1. Perfect competition involves more than the absence of governmental interferences. Adam Smith recognized the need for many governmental activities to make competition workable. We shall consider some of these in Part 4.

2. Perfect competition exists only when each unit of each good is priced at the marginal cost of producing and marketing. This includes no allowance for overhead. The marginal cost of producing and selling a certain book might be less than one dollar. But if the publisher sold its books at marginal

---

[4] A. C. Pigou, *The Economics of Welfare*. New York: St. Martin's Press, Inc.
[5] Paul A. Samuelson, *Foundations of Economic Analysis*. Cambridge, Mass.: Harvard University Press, 1947.
[6] Willard W. Cochrane, *Farm Prices: Myth and Reality*. Minneapolis: University of Minnesota Press, 1958, p. 3.

cost, it would go bankrupt. So would the railroads, the automobile companies—even the universities—if they all disregarded their overhead costs in setting prices. Only a socialistic society could use modern methods of production if all prices were to be at marginal cost. It would not be concerned with the profits of nationalized industries, since losses could be repaid from taxes.

3. Private monopolies could, however, make profits and sell their *marginal output* at a *marginal price* equal to marginal cost. Theoretically, this would give the same allocation of resources—and the same outputs—as would occur if the entire output were sold at marginal cost and if high-overhead industries were subsidized. A French engineer-economist, Dupuit,[7] made a good defense for perfect price discrimination on these grounds.

4. If the perfect market were accepted as the best possible solution, this would not mean that any one industry—agriculture, for example—should move toward a free market unless the markets for other industries and for labor were perfect.

5. All justifications of the perfect market and the invisible hand are based upon one of three assumptions: (a) that the existing distribution of income between families is ideal, or (b) that nothing can be done to change income distribution, or (c) that income distribution is a separate subject, to be dealt with by welfare programs that do not interfere with free market prices.

Perhaps there is something to say for (c). But so long as poverty exists, why pretend that we get the best possible result when people "vote with their dollars"? Should economists condemn a food-stamp program for low-income families on the grounds that, instead, we should eliminate poverty? Is the best allocation of resources one which lets millions of unemployed persons go hungry while we have food surpluses—simply because some well-meaning economist hopes that unemployment may go away some time in the future?

Perhaps we have said enough to make you a little skeptical

---

[7] See Frederick V. Waugh, *Readings on Agricultural Marketing*. Ames: Iowa State College Press, 1954, p. 331.

about broad claims that a free market would necessarily solve all economic problems. If so, we have accomplished our purpose. We believe this skepticism is warranted. But skepticism alone is a negative sort of virtue. We hasten to say that we think there is great merit in private industry and in competition. They have brought us prosperity in the past, and will continue to do so in the future. The urge for personal profit is a powerful incentive to economic development and expansion. But this does not necessarily mean that all departures from a free market are to be condemned. Especially in a democracy, the voters have a right to determine economic goals. A competent economist may show them how to reach these goals, but he won't get far by scolding them for picking the wrong goals.

The farm economist would do well to consider proposed farm programs on their own merits—not just to repeat ancient slogans based upon half-understood doctrines. Too many administrators react to every new proposal by saying, "It won't work." Too many alleged economists are against all industry or government programs because they interfere with "the optimum allocation of resources"—usually meaning the "perfect market." A really good economist will not be satisfied with fancy words and easy slogans as a substitute for thought. If he opposes a proposal, he will have good, solid, understandable, straightforward reasons for his opposition.

QUESTIONS FOR DISCUSSION

1. What is perfect competition? Do the markets for raw-form products (wheat, cotton, hogs) more nearly, or less nearly, meet the definition of perfect competition than do the markets for processed goods (bread, cloth, ham)?

2. How would you define the most efficient use of our resources?

3. Do you think our economic resources would be used more efficiently under conditions approaching perfect competition—or under a benevolent and wise socialism? Why?

SUPPLEMENTARY READING

1. Bain, Joe S., *Pricing, Distribution, and Employment.* New York: Henry Holt and Company, 1955, Ch. 4.

2. Lerner, Abba, *The Economics of Control.* New York: The Macmillan Company, 1944.
3. Marshall, Alfred, *Principles of Economics.* New York: The Macmillan Company, 8th ed., 1949, Book V, Chs. 1, 2, and 3.
4. Marx, Karl, *Capital.* New York: Modern Library, 1948. (This is a tedious book; the student need not read much of it. But Marx made a scholarly attack on the kind of competition that existed in his day, and advanced a learned argument for state socialism.)
5. Shepherd, G. S., *Agricultural Price Policy.* Ames: Iowa State College Press, 1947, Chs. 18 and 19.
6. Smith, Adam, *An Inquiry into the Nature and Causes of the Wealth of Nations.* New York: Modern Library, 1937.

7

The Principle of
Comparative Advantage

Professor Black wrote,[1] "The Principle of Comparative Advantage is the most difficult of all economic principles to state." Black devoted six chapters (142 pages) of his book to a discussion of "Specialization and Comparative Advantage." Here we shall take less space. But we shall try to present the basic principle.

Since the full statement is difficult, let us first state the principle only as it applies to the decisions made by individuals or firms. Later, we shall consider the principle as applied to areas or countries.

The general idea is simple and rather obvious. *Any intelligent person who has a choice between two alternatives will consider the probable advantages and disadvantages of each and will choose the alternative which he thinks is likely to give him the greater net advantage.*

This is perhaps rather vague. Suppose we make it more concrete by considering only *monetary* advantages and disadvantages—in other words, income and expenses. Then our principle could be written: *if a person has a choice between two alternatives and wishes to choose the one which is likely to be most profitable to him, he must consider the probable income and probable expenses of each alternative and will choose the one for which his net income (gross income minus expenses) is likely to be greater.*

---

[1] John D. Black, *Production Economics*. New York: Henry Holt and Co., 1926, p. 136.

Although this second statement is more concrete than the first, it is not so general. If monetary profit were the only thing in life, this would not make any difference. Then "advantage" would be synonymous with "money income" and "disadvantage" would mean "monetary cost." In actual life, money is not the only motivation—although it is obviously one of the most powerful. The farmer, the middleman, and even the doctor and the preacher usually want to increase their net incomes. And when they try to do this, they are following the simpler (second) statement of the principle of comparative advantage. But the first statement is broader. It includes less tangible advantages, such as the social prestige associated with certain professions and the desire for fame rather than fortune. It includes less tangible disadvantages, too—the boredom associated with life on a backwoods farm and the physical discomfort from weeding onions on your hands and knees.

Take a simple example. Two poultry farmers in Connecticut are now peddling their eggs from door to door. Both are thinking of joining a co-operative association. This would enable them to stop peddling their eggs and would give them more time to spend on production. They could handle more layers and have more eggs to sell, but, of course, they would get a lower price. Instead of getting the retail price, they would get the wholesale price minus a deduction to cover the expenses of the association.

These two men have done some figuring, with the help of their county agent and the state extension economist. They agree that both could make a larger net income by joining the association—that is, that they could increase production more than enough to offset lower prices, and that their total costs (production and marketing, together) would be no higher than before. The first man joins the association because he is interested mainly in the more limited (monetary) aspects of comparative advantage. The second man continues to peddle eggs—not because he expects to make more money, but because he likes to see people. In other words, the expected increase in monetary income is not enough to compensate him for the reduction in social contact. This man, too, is following the principle of comparative advantage, but he is considering the nonmonetary aspects covered in the broader statement.

The economy of the world has been shaped largely by decisions concerning comparative advantage. Many of these decisions are individual, personal. Many are made by officers of corporations on the basis of comparative advantage to the stockholders. Others are made by governments, partly at least on the basis of presumed comparative advantage to the people.

In general, most such decisions have tended to result in greater specialization—both between persons and between areas. Each person, and each area, has certain inherent advantages and limitations. It is generally more profitable for an individual or an area to specialize in a few things in order to capitalize his advantages and not be handicapped by his limitations. Wisconsin has many advantages in dairying but is not well-adapted to the production of peaches. This state is better off to concentrate on dairying and buy her peaches from Georgia. This may seem obvious, but it is surprising how often such simple ideas are overlooked—especially when considering international trade.

In some cases an area may not have a real advantage in anything. Its soil and climate may be poor. It may be far from the market. But, at least, its disadvantages may be less along some lines than along others. Black[2] gives the following illustration, in which "the numbers represent assumed returns per unit of production elements in the two countries":

	United States	Italy
Wheat	40	30
Corn	50	10

In this purely illustrative example, Italy is presumed to be at a disadvantage, compared to the United States, both in wheat and in corn. But Italy's disadvantage is much less for wheat than for corn. So, as Black wrote, "If the United States and Italy were the only two countries in the world, Italy under the foregoing assumptions would surely specialize in wheat and the United States in corn. *Comparison of returns*

---

2 John D. Black, *op. cit.*, p. 132.

must be made not only between countries, but between different products in each country."

Thus, each person and each area tends to specialize in those things for which it has the greatest advantages, or the least disadvantages, compared with other persons or areas. There are, of course, many difficulties, such as that of defining a "unit of production elements." Such a unit would have to be some composite of acres of land, man-hours of work, and amounts of capital. These difficulties are inherent in the subject. But each person, in each area, is guided in his economic decisions by his understanding of the principle of comparative advantage.

It is this principle that is mainly responsible for the existence of agricultural marketing as a separate business or profession. In colonial America each family produced most of its own food and clothing. Gradually, American farmers have learned to specialize more and more. Nowadays, a typical potato farmer in Aroostook County, Maine, has no vegetable garden, no chickens, no cows—he sells potatoes and buys all the other foods he needs. And he makes a much better living in this way. He could not do this unless thousands of other people had specialized in marketing. These thousands of other people not only sell the potatoes produced by our Aroostook County farmer; they also process, store, transport, and sell the thousands of items that he buys.

Again, it is this principle that explains specialization within the field of marketing. The typical marketing firm handles only a few commodities—grain or dairy products. Or it performs only a few services—perhaps storing, packaging, or wholesaling. During World War II, the O.P.A. hired a food marketing man who turned out to be a pickle expert. But the first pickle problem that came up happened to involve sour pickles, and this man knew only about sweet pickles. But even this man might have been more specialized. Suppose he were an expert in packages for sweet watermelon pickles?

Doubtless specialization can be carried too far. It has its own dangers—and its counter-pressures toward diversification. But the principle of comparative advantage exerts a powerful force toward greater specialization—both between persons and between areas. Many governments resist this pressure—partly to protect farmers from foreign competition, and partly to be prepared for war. But governments also do many things to help the principle work better. This includes much of the government work on statistics, market information, and research in methods of production and marketing. We shall consider some of these matters in Part 4 of this book.

We have not spelled out the principle of comparative advantage in detail. Actual economic life is extremely complicated. Most decisions involve comparisons of advantages not between two persons or areas, but among several; not between two alternative actions, but among several. But an understanding of the two-person, two-commodity problem will help greatly to clarify the more complex problems. After all, the *n*-person, *n*-commodity problem, complicated as it is, is no more than a long series of two-person, two-commodity problems.

In fact, decision-making in actual life is what mathematicians call an "iterative" process—that is, decisions are made one step at a time. Perhaps no one can have enough information about all possible lines of action to figure out which one will maximize his advantages or minimize his disadvantages. But he can usually judge fairly accurately whether it is feasible for him to make a change that will *improve* his situation. The farmer has learned to do this by the "budget method," which enables him to estimate how his net income would change if he shifted small amounts of land, labor, or capital from their present uses to other uses. The recently developed techniques of linear programming have made it possible to make such computations systematically. For some economic problems, at least, it is not quite feasible to carry out an iterative process to the last step where no further improvements are possible.

We end this brief discussion, therefore, with an attempt to define an improvement in comparative advantage:

A person, or an area, can improve its comparative advantage if it can shift any of its productive inputs (that is, land, labor, or capital) from present uses to others and expect to make a more satisfactory living—whether by getting a larger monetary profit, or by increasing its nonmonetary satisfactions.

Furthermore, *if all such improvements have been made, a person, or an area, has maximized its comparative advantage.*

Probably few persons or areas ever reach an absolute maximum in real life. We progress slowly and fumblingly. But one of the outstanding facts about the economic history of the world is that economic progress has come in large measure through the specialization that has resulted from constant efforts to capitalize on comparative advantage.

QUESTIONS FOR DISCUSSION

1. What are the leading farm enterprises in your state? Do farmers in your state have certain advantages over those in other states in the production or marketing of the products in which they specialize?

2. Farmers located near New York, Chicago, and San Francisco obviously have certain advantages in the marketing of almost any product. Yet they don't produce many beef cattle, nor wheat. Why is this?

3. Describe a situation in which you have made a choice between two alternatives by using the principle of comparative advantage.

SUPPLEMENTARY READING

1. Black, John D., *Production Economics*. New York: Henry Holt and Company, 1926, pp. 132-136.
2. Fetter, F. A., "The Economic Loss of Market Areas," *Quarterly Journal of Economics*, May, 1924.
3. Marsh, D. B., *World Trade and Investment*. New York: Harcourt, Brace and Company, 1951.

PART 2

COSTS AND ALLOCATIONS

8

Keeping Costs Down

The present chapter deals with some examples of costs and of cost-saving methods available to modern plants and firms handling agricultural products.

Physical Handling

"Processing" means changing the form of the farm product. Many of these operations for fruits and vegetables, such as cleaning, topping of carrots, packing of lettuce or apples, are done at the farm. For products like wheat, cotton, tobacco, pork, beef, and frozen orange juice, however, some specialized processing is required which cannot be done at the farm. Industries have been developed for the purpose of processing agricultural products. Meat packing, cotton ginning, milk bottling, and flour milling are examples. Numerous others will come to mind as one thinks of all the processed items that are available in a modern retail food store.

There is a story of man-hours of labor and of machines behind that neatly wrapped loaf of bread and those boxes of breakfast cereal. Wheat grown on the western plains is trucked by a farmer to a local elevator. The elevator company stores the grain, and a miller in Buffalo orders two carloads. This grain is loaded from the elevator to rail cars and shipped to Buffalo. There it is stored until ready for use. The grain is transferred from storage to the mill. There the wheat is cleaned, ground, and several types of flour and by-products and bran or middlings produced. The flour is bagged and sold to a bakery in Boston. There it is made into rolls and bread. From the baker, it is trucked to the retail store or the home. The whole system is a combination of transporting, storing, handling, processing, and selling.

The costs are marketing costs. A long distance means high transportation charges. A refined product means more processing costs than for an unrefined product. A process requiring a great deal of labor or other ingredients will probably cost more than one in which labor use is small and the process simple. Delivery to the home will cost more than delivery to a store. It is estimated that wheat growers receive less than 20 cents of the final retail dollar for wheat sold as bread. The remainder goes to the processing and marketing agencies. This proportion varies with the amount of processing and transportation involved.

Costs Are a Combination of Services and Jobs

Apples are packed in lugs or boxes and stacked by the pickers. The lugs are loaded onto a truck or trailer and hauled to the plant. After weighing, the men unload the full lugs.

The apples are washed and then inspected and graded for packing or for diversion to processing. Sorting tables are generally used, equipped with belt conveyors. After sorting, the job of packing is to place the fruit in boxes so as to minimize damage and to present an attractive pack. The boxes are lidded and stamped, and then stacked in cold storage. For delivery, they are hauled out of storage and loaded onto a conveyor truck for shipment.

Beef cattle are hauled from the feed lot by truck to a packing plant or they are hauled by rail to a terminal yard, where the animal is sold, transferred to another means of conveyance and delivered to the packing plant. The animal is slaughtered, skinned, cleaned and the carcass graded. Further cutting and handling are required before it is ready for the wholesaler and the retailer.

The carcass may then move to a sausage or wiener manufacturer. The meat is boned by butchers, and is ground and mixed with spices and other condiments. The mixture goes through machines to make wieners. These are then hung in smoke rooms to cure. From there they are taken to be packed and stored for later sale.

Cost Analysis

Holding down costs through efficient operations is essential to making the greatest profit. But it is only part of the picture. Profit is the difference between total costs and total returns from sale of products. It is possible to perform each operation efficiently and still operate at a loss. This is partly a matter of sales and revenue—and this will be discussed later. But it is also a matter of the level of operations—what volume to put through a plant, and, perhaps, even more important, what size of plant to operate in the first place.

To make an intelligent decision on this, it is necessary to study the structure of costs, and the principles that determine how they vary with volume or scale of operation—both in an established plant and in plants of various sizes. Then we can compare costs with returns at various outputs to determine the most profitable volume to plan for.

TOTAL COSTS

The costs of production include the costs of buildings, equipment, and land, which in the short run we shall refer to as *fixed costs*. The costs of material, of power, and of labor, which vary with the amount of product handled, will be called *variable costs*.

In Figure 1 total costs are represented on the vertical axis and total produced on the horizontal axis. The total fixed costs OA remain constant at all levels of output OD. The variable costs AC increase as output increases from O to D.

$$\text{Total Cost} = \text{Fixed Cost} + \text{Variable Cost}$$

Therefore, total cost at output OD is DC.

AVERAGE COSTS

The cost per unit of product can be derived by dividing the total cost by the total number of units produced. As fixed costs are a part of total costs, the average costs per unit can be reduced by increasing output. This will be true up to the point where the fixed investment is fully utilized at out-

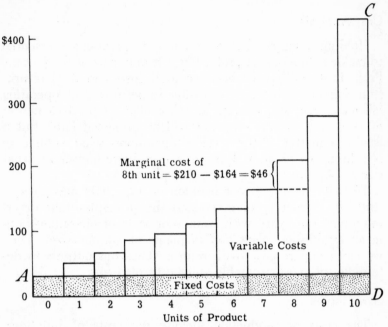

Figure 1.

put *OD* in Figure 1. Beyond this point, diseconomies owing to overcrowding or to overuse of machinery and the extra management needed will increase average unit costs.

MARGINAL COST

The cost which has the most significance to the plant owner is the marginal cost. It is the relationship between this cost and the selling price that determines the most profitable output of his enterprise. *The marginal cost is the addition to costs required to produce an extra unit of product.* Fixed, variable, total, and marginal costs are illustrated in Table 1. Total, or fixed, cost remains the same throughout the operation. Total variable cost increases as each additional quantity is produced and establishes the rate at which total cost increases. Marginal cost is the change in total cost for each additional unit of production. In Figure 1, and in Table 1, we consider the "discrete" case, where output can be adjusted only by whole units (that is, it can be raised from 4 units to 5 units, but not to 4⅔ units, for example). In the present case, costs go up in jumps, not continuously. We shall discuss continuous curves on pages 118 to 121.

Table 1

Fixed, Variable, Total and Marginal Costs

Units of Product	Fixed Cost	Variable Cost	Total Cost	Average Cost	Marginal Cost
0	30	0	30		
1	30	20	50	50	20
2	30	38	68	34	18
3	30	51	81	27	13
4	30	64	94	23	13
5	30	80	110	22	16
6	30	102	132	22	22
7	30	134	164	23	32
8	30	180	210	26	46
9	30	249	279	31	69
10	30	400	430	43	151

RELATIONSHIP BETWEEN AVERAGE, MARGINAL, AND TOTAL COSTS

The relationship of the costs of a firm can be shown graphically as in Figure 2. Here average cost declines to a minimum point at output *OD* (considering only integral units of output). At this point also marginal costs are equal to average cost. In Table 1, this would be at six units of product.

Average cost is the total cost divided by the units of product, and marginal cost is the additional cost associated with the last unit of output.

To Reduce Costs

An owner or manager of a processing establishment aims to increase his net income and profits while at the same time meeting competition from rivals. One means of attaining this end is to reduce total costs. Each of the stages in his plant involves the use of labor and machines. The cost of a machine is the initial purchase price amortized over its useful life, plus operating charges. The cost of labor is the wages paid for the time and work that individuals contribute. Rent, electricity,

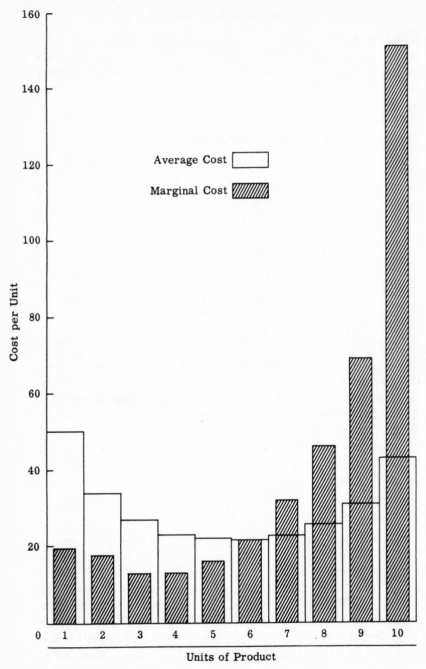

Figure 2.

76

and water are other costs, some fixed, some varying with level of operations.

There will be no incentive for workers to introduce time-saving methods of doing their jobs unless returns for their labor are increased. There will be no incentive for the man who pays the wages to adopt new methods if the labor output cannot be increased at the same cost, or if the same job cannot be accomplished with less labor. The incentive is provided by the potential increase in profits. A reduction in market costs is then possible by a combination of incentives and methods.

To Reduce Time and Motion

(A) THE INDIVIDUAL JOB

There are numerous ways in which particular jobs can be done, just as there is variation in the time each takes. Before suggesting ways of reducing the time and effort to do any particular job, it is first necessary to analyze the job and the operations involved. One method of obtaining this information is work sampling.[2] Records of the proportion of time spent by individuals and by machines for various jobs are established. This may be done by observing each worker at repeated intervals, to obtain a breakdown of "working" and "nonworking" time for each job. The percentage that "working" time is of the total time gives the "ratio-delay" index as a measure of efficiency for labor or machines. This will provide a guide for preventing an undue proportion of delays and for an improvement in techniques of handling or processing. It is a good substitute for the stop-watch technique of time studies, which, by the use of a stop watch and photos, records each stage or job in the accomplishment of an end product, after which the photos are shown on the screen at slow speed and subjected to certain tests.

This method is applicable to work performed in repetitive cycles. If the task is divided into a series of discrete elements,

---

[2] L. L. Sammet and J. B. Hessler, "Use of the Ratio-Delay Method in Processing Plant Operations," *Agric. Economics Research*, Vol. III, No. 4, U.S.D.A.

the analysis may lead to changes in the equipment or in the work methods.

Frank G. Gilbreth, at the end of the nineteenth century, was one of the earliest American students of motion and time in the accomplishment of production jobs. He appreciated the gains that could be attained by minimizing effort and by making full use of time on the job.

There are certain basic motions in a cycle of actions, which Gilbreth called "therbligs" (which you will note is his name spelled backwards). These "therbligs" are listed as *search, find, select, grasp, transport loaded, position, assemble, use, disassemble, inspect, pre-position, release load, transport empty, rest, delay, plan, hold.*

Analysis of these stages may provide more adequate and quicker methods of accomplishment. For example, *search* by an operator for a tool or material used on the job can be eliminated or reduced by keeping all items to be used within arm's reach or in some particular place. *Grasp* will be used for picking up any object and various types of equipment for grasping may be substituted for that now used. "Transport loaded" is related to the size and weight of the object. Can tools be placed for easy grasp? and, Is the article transferred from one hand to the other unnecessarily? are typical questions which should be answered and which may lead to simplified techniques. Perhaps an object should be slid rather than carried, or perhaps "transport empty" can be eliminated.

By means of work sampling and time-and-motion studies it is possible to establish average or standard times for each job and for the total process. Deviations from this standard may indicate bottlenecks or other inefficiencies which can be eliminated by reorganization of the jobs or of the timing.

The calculation of standards and their use in job analysis must take into consideration variations in conditions, in capacity of labor, and in the wages paid. They should be used only as guides to efficiency and not as ironclad rules.

(B) THE PLANT LAYOUT

Study of the individual jobs will probably reveal unnecessary motion which is time-consuming and costly and which can be eliminated by rearrangement of equipment or points of loading and unloading. In this way the flow of material through successive stages can be improved, to reduce carrying and loss of time.

In the broiler dressing plant described on page 35, one employee can eviscerate 48 birds per hour, another can cool, size, and package 133 birds per hour. Simple arithmetic shows that 25 eviscerators are needed for 9 packagers if both types of operators are to be kept continuously busy. The same principle applies in determining relationships among other operations. Efficient plant layout requires planning such relationships and arranging equipment so that birds flow from one operation to another without waste motion.

(c) THE BEST COMBINATION

Such technical considerations determine the most efficient organization of a given plant process. Choice between alternative processing methods depends upon relative input prices: materials costs, wage rates, machinery prices, etc. Management seeks the combination that will minimize unit cost of the product under the particular situation it faces.

This combination will change as the prices of the production factors change. For example, an increase in wages may be sufficient to justify the purchase of an additional piece of equipment in order to reduce labor requirements. This would be substituting machinery for labor. Similarly, the prices of the raw materials used in production may change, and one material can be substituted for another.

In a dynamic market, it is apparent that, with prices and costs continually changing, the management must be prepared continually to change the methods of production and the combination of labor, equipment, and space if it is to obtain the greatest possible production at the lowest cost.

It must be able to calculate fairly accurately the effect on production of hiring another man, and to compare the increased cost with the increased returns expected. It must be able to measure the effect on costs and returns of adding another piece of equipment or of hiring more space. This problem is similar to that of the feed manufacturer, who studies changes in prices of dozens of ingredients, and seeks the lowest-cost mixture that meets certain specifications. Theoretically, it can be solved by linear-programming methods if the basic input-output coefficients are known.

A Model Plant

A useful technique for planning jobs in processing, handling, and transportation is to build model plants. To plan successfully, a thorough knowledge of the time to do specific jobs, of the capacity of machinery, and of the properties of the supplies used is essential. By the use of budgets, various combinations and methods are tested by trial and error to establish the lowest-cost, highest-production plan. To build satisfactory models may require complete abandonment of given operations and the adoption of different technologies, or it may require little or no change in existing operations. After adjusting the model to prevailing costs, prices, and production conditions, the management is provided with a plan for comparison with its present plant or for building a new one.

Size is one of the most important variables in the cost of operation. The more extensively buildings, machines, or other equipment can be used, the lower the average cost for each unit of product. Under-utilization of plant will result in higher average costs than those attainable by increased use. Similarly, over-utilization, which causes crowding or otherwise slows down operations, will increase average costs.

Quality of Product

An important phase of many physical handling operations is the effect on *quality* of the product. Methods that reduce labor requirements or speed up the operation of machines may represent false economies if these savings result in a sacrifice of quality—through bruising or exposure to unsanitary conditions or less careful culling or trimming. The general problem of quality in relation to value of products—how it is identified, measured, and taken account of in trade—will be discussed in a later chapter. Here are outlined some operational procedures for keeping watch on quality and making sure that specified standards are adhered to.

The taste, sight, feel, and smell of a product are constituents of quality and as such are an important part of any production process. A poor-quality product to start with can rarely be transformed into a high-quality product within the plant. The first requirement for a high-quality product of farm produce is that it be received free from bruises, damage, or spoilage.

What happens after a product starts along the line to be cured, canned, or frozen becomes a responsibility of the plant manager. The acceptance of a product by consumers and the confidence that consumers will place in his particular brand or type of product will influence the profit position of the operation and the increase or decrease in future business.

QUALITY CONTROLS

For this reason, it is important that quality controls be established. In a fruit-canning operation, for example, the method of handling, the rate of bruising, and the syrup content are established. It is essential to the seller and the buyer that the final product be uniform. Errors in process are possible and probable in the best of operations. Therefore, a check is to open some of the cans before sale, to see if they meet the specifications claimed by the seller. Certainly not every can of frozen pack can be opened any more than every bag of flour or every package of breakfast food.

SAMPLING THE PRODUCT

This, then, becomes a problem in sampling. From each batch of product, some are selected for inspection. In the simplest systems of quality control, a lot is rejected if a certain number of items fail to meet specifications. In more complicated systems of "sequential sampling," the first inspection may lead to rejection or to acceptance of the lot, or to the inspection of a new sample.

The buying of large quantities of fruit, cotton, beef animals, or wheat from a particular wholesaler or assembler is subject to similar variations in quality. A buyer may protect himself by agreeing on a particular sampling method before purchasing. If the samples fall within particular limits, then the purchase is completed. If not, then a lower price and grade may be the outcome. For example, wheat moving into trade in Canada is sampled in transit and graded by government inspectors after the samples are examined and tested for certain grade and quality characteristics. Distant buyers of these grades are assured of their purchases meeting certain agreed standards and characteristics. Sampling and testing may be done by a *buyer*, as a basis for accepting or rejecting a shipment; but, especially at retail, the buyer usually accepts without test, and simply buys a different brand next time if he is not satisfied. Hence the importance to the processor of himself sampling and testing to be sure that his product meets standards of acceptability.

A product may be spot-checked during the assembly-line process and samples taken at each stage. This is a form of production control. It may be possible to screen every item as it moves in the line and to remove defective units. In the manufacture of canned meat products or of flour or cotton goods, however, the units may require individual inspection and testing which would not be possible during the production process. Buyers' insistence on a spot sample check would provide incentive for the processor to safeguard against product deterioration in his plant. Particularly would this be true if lots were rejected frequently.

Hire an Efficiency Expert

The management of a plant or a store that handles food products must make decisions on the use of its factors of production such as labor, machinery, floor space, and building. How they are combined will not only affect the final cost position of the product but will be a measure of the managerial ability of the manager.

The process of making decisions, however, can be improved if all available information is assembled and all possible technical assistance is used. This is the age of specialization, and no one manager can be expected to keep abreast of all fields related to his operations. There are engineers specializing in the efficiency of machines; there are specialists in plant layout, quality control, and so on. Perhaps it would be profitable to hire an efficiency expert for consultation on one or more of these phases of the plant operation. Failing this, visits and discussions with other managers and operators may provide useful background for making decisions in any particular plant.

The Co-operative Extension Service provides facilities for learning at meetings or by consultation and advice from their experts. Publications from the state colleges and trade organizations also provide information on how to reduce costs.

Studies may show levels of cost and efficiency achieved by similar stores or plants as a whole, or for various phases of operation. Comparison of a manager's own results with these gives some indication of weak spots and would be advantageous when obtaining expert help.

Balancing Costs and Income for the Greatest Profit

The extent to which cost-reducing methods are to be adopted will depend on the profit incentives for such action. These, in turn, will depend on the potential revenue from sales at various levels of operation. The best size has to be adopted to gain the greatest profit. For this reason, the management must consider potential revenue in relation to costs and to size of opertaion in order to make the best decision.

MARGINAL REVENUE

Marginal revenue is the additional revenue received from the sale of each additional unit of product. Here, as on page 74, we are concerned with discrete changes in revenue, and not with a smooth revenue curve. For example, Table 2 shows the relationship between quantity sold, price, and revenue.

The price here is assumed to decline as sales increase. Therefore, total revenue first increases up to six units of product and then decreases. Marginal revenue measures the change in total revenue.

TO MAXIMIZE PROFIT

If now we combine the costs from Table 1 with the revenue

figures from Table 2, it will be possible to decide on the output that will maximize profit.

Table 2

Marginal Revenue and Price

Quantity	Price	Total Revenue	Marginal Revenue
1	56	56	56
2	51	102	46
3	46	138	36
4	41	164	26
5	36	180	16
6	31	186	6
7	26	182	− 4
8	21	168	−14
9	16	144	−24
10	11	110	−34

Table 3

Revenue, Cost, and Profit

Quantity	Total Revenue	Total Cost	Profit	Marginal Revenue	Marginal Cost
0	0	30	− 30		
1	56	50	6	56	20
2	102	68	34	46	18
3	138	81	57	36	13
4	164	94	70	26	13
5	180	110	70	16	16
6	186	132	54	6	22
7	182	164	18	− 4	32
8	168	210	− 42	−14	46
9	144	279	−135	−24	69
10	110	430	−320	−34	151

As quantity produced and sold increases from four to five units, the marginal revenue equals the marginal cost. The cost of the fifth unit is equal to the revenue from the sale of this unit. Beyond this point, marginal revenue declines and marginal cost increases. Profit at both four and five units of output is the highest at 70. (We assume here that it is not possible to produce and sell 4½ units.) See Table 3 and Figure 3.

It is this level of output with these prices that will be most profitable for the firm. Here, then, is a guide to measuring that scale of production that will maximize profits. In a competitive market, the prices are established by supply and demand at any particular time, and it may not be possible to

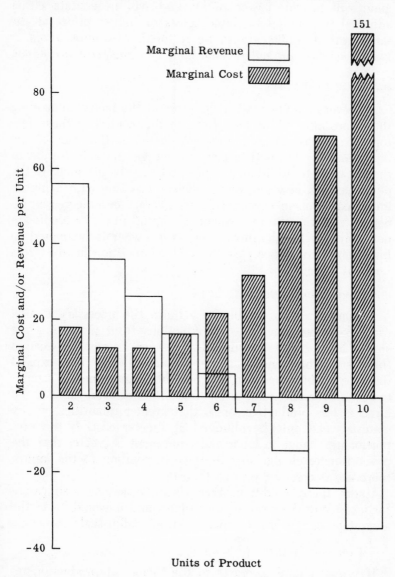

Figure 3.

forecast the exact market price at which a product will be sold at some future date. However, sale of a product at a price that results in marginal cost greater than marginal revenue will provide lower profits and will necessitate either adjusted production to reduce costs or higher prices at the same cost if profits are to be restored. *Maximum profit is gained when marginal revenue and marginal cost are equal.*

SCALE OF OPERATION

A decrease in costs, with the price of the factors remaining the same, may be attained by a reorganization of those factors into different combinations. A decline in the price of one input relative to another may encourage the substitution of the cheaper. In addition, a lower cost may be attained by the purchase of a new and more efficient machine with a higher initial cost but an expected future average-cost decrease sufficient to justify the investment. If capital funds or credit are not available for this investment, the owner is hampered in his attempt to reduce costs, so that competition finally forces him out of business.

Decreasing Returns to Scale

A manager who is able to acquire the necessary capital can take advantage of cost reductions from increasing the size of his operation. To do this, however, he must be assured that he will have increasing returns to scale. He may expand the size of his operation so that the management becomes too much for one man, or so that the additional labor to be hired is less productive, or so that greater quantities of raw materials can only be obtained at greater cost. If the proportionate change in labor and equipment is greater than the proportionate change in output corresponding to the inputs, there are decreasing returns to scale.

Under these conditions there is no economic justification for increasing the scale of operations, and it would be to the advantage of the firm to operate on a smaller scale.

Constant Returns to Scale

If proportionate increases in the factors of production resulted in equal proportionate increases in product, we would have a condition of constant returns to scale. This would imply that there were no fixed factors and that all the factors of production of inputs were equally flexible or divisible into small units. Such a condition might exist if we assumed no changes in technology or in prices.

Increasing Returns to Scale

The greatest justification for increasing the size of a firm is the possibility of obtaining proportionately greater increases in output than the proportionate change in input. By obtaining more product per input, the average cost would be reduced and the profit position of the firm improved. The problem, as before, is to arrive at that size of plant and that combination of production factors (land, labor, and capital) that will permit a product to be produced at the lowest possible cost per unit. A "model" plant will facilitate planning. Different-size plants can be budgeted to estimate the effect of size increase on unit costs. An illustration of the development of a planning curve from average cost curves for plant models of various sizes is shown in Figure 4.

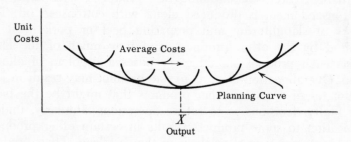

Figure 4.

The envelope curve which connects the average cost curves will indicate to the planner the sizes of budgeted plants that will minimize the total cost of the industry. On the basis of these calculations, the owners may then plan for expansion or contraction of existing facilities.

The decision by the management to increase scale is rational if based on expected lower unit costs or on increased profits. However, if increase in size is attempted merely for the sake of handling more product, there is every possibility that the competitive position of the firm will deteriorate.

Other Limits to Size

The flexibility of the production factors which make possible increasing returns to scale cannot go on indefinitely without meeting some rigidity of obstruction that provides a fixed factor. Once a fixed factor exists, decreasing returns follow. Such a fixed factor may be the managerial ability of the owner or the decision-making powers of a group of owners. The business could become unwieldly with a top-heavy growth of management and increased problems of supervision and labor relations.

COST ALLOCATIONS

In the calculation of costs, difficulties frequently arise because the agricultural raw material is used for the production of numerous products. Milk is delivered to the plant and joint products, such as bottled fluid milk, ice cream, cream, and cheese are made from the milk. Hides are produced along with beef carcasses, middlings are produced with flour, and cottonseed meal is produced along with cottonseed oil. The costs of slaughtering and preparing beef or pork must be shared by the other products, and how much of the fixed costs each product should carry poses a problem of allocation. Overallocation of costs to one product may result in low estimates of costs for other products that might be the basis for faulty decisions as to future operations. Similarly, under-allocation to some products results in certain other products carrying more than their share of the cost load. Their production then appears less profitable than it really is, and decisions of the owner will be influenced accordingly. There are no simple, universally valid rules for allocating costs between joint products.

A New Plant for the Old

Farmers, processors, and distributors are continually challenged to keep up to date in production methods. This is a result of changes in the type of product requirements, shifts in the location of markets, new techniques of production, and the need for cost reduction—all characteristics of our competitive system.

The owner or board of directors makes decisions on purchases of new equipment, additions to buildings, the size of the business, and plans for expansion. There may come a time when it is necessary to make the basic and important decision whether to stay in business in that location and with that particular plant or to secure a new plant and location that would be more profitable.

Radical changes in production methods may necessitate changes in plant layout and location of equipment. Building additions or alterations costs money. The cost of alterations plus depreciation on the old buildings must be compared with the cost of completely new buildings before a decision is made. If a new building is under consideration, it may be a good chance to move to a more suitable location. Probably there have been many changes in the surrounding area since the plant was first built. Trucking and unloading facilities may be more crowded, and the market may have changed its location and density. A very important decision would involve the movement of a plant out of the region to another section of the country. The movement of a mill from New England to the South is an example.

In all cases of such decisions, it is necessary to understand the cost structure of the plant and the firm and to appreciate the relationship of cost to size and location.

QUESTIONS FOR DISCUSSION

1. Construct a total cost curve and from it derive the average and marginal costs for two levels of production.
2. What determines the most profitable output at which to operate?
3. What is the relationship of scale of output to unit cost of production?
4. Can a business become so large that it is inefficient?
5. Outline a plan to discover ways of reducing costs in a food-

processing plant of your choice. (Assume no changes in the present plant nor in its equipment.)

6. Outline a plan for discovering cost-saving changes in the plant or in its equipment.

7. What is a model plant, and what are the advantages of using such a model?

8. What are the reasons for sampling a product?

9. Would an increase in wage rates change the most profitable operation of a plant: (a) In the short run? (b) In the long run?

SUPPLEMENTARY READING

1. Bain, Joe S., *Pricing, Distribution, and Employment.* New York: Henry Holt and Company, 1953, Ch. 3.
2. Boulding, Kenneth E., *Economic Analysis.* New York: Harper & Brothers, 1948, Ch. 31.
3. Bressler, R. G., Jr., "Economies of Scale in the Operation of Country Milk Plants." Boston: New England Research Council, 1942.
4. Brunk, Max E., "An Economic Study of Celery Marketing," Bul. 445, University of Florida, Agr. Expt. Sta.
5. Cornell, W. B., and H. Madeheim, *Organization and Management in Industry and Business.* New York: Ronald Press Company, 1958, Ch. 7.
6. Freeman, H. A., M. Friedman, *et al., Sampling Inspection.* New York: McGraw-Hill Book Company, Inc., 1948, Ch. 5.
7. French, B. C., L. L. Sammet, and R. G. Bressler, "Economic Efficiency in Plant Operations with Special Reference to the Marketing of California Pears," *Hilgardia,* Vol. 24, No. 19, July, 1956.
8. Sammet, L. L., and B. C. French, "Economic Engineering Methods in Marketing Research," *Journal of Farm Economics,* Vol. XXXV, 1953, No. 5.
9. Sammet, L. L., and J. R. Hassler, "Use of the Ratio-Delay Method in Processing Plant Operations," *Agricultural Economics Research,* Vol. III, No. 4, Washington, D.C.: U. S. Department of Agriculture.

9

Market Development

The term "market development" covers all efforts to raise the demand for a commodity—whether by advertising, promotion, subsidy, the invention of new products, or any other means. Today, market development is one of the most interesting and controversial aspects of agricultural marketing. Some enthusiasts believe that agricultural surpluses would disappear promptly and completely if we only had an active program to encourage industrial uses, or if we stepped up our present program to develop export outlets. But not all economists are counted among the enthusiasts for such programs— whether carried out by government or by private industry.

Before discussing these matters in detail, we shall consider briefly the nature of demand.

Consumer Demand

Since Alfred Marshall, the usual discussion of consumer demand starts with the demand of an individual family. But each individual family's demand is affected by peculiar preferences, attitudes, and habits that are hard to understand. Here we are concerned mainly with the sum of the demands of all consumers in a market, that is, with market demand in terms of retail prices.

Economists have long known that the amount of a commodity purchased by consumers depends in large measure upon two factors: first, the price of the commodity; second, the income of consumers. Since the early 1920's, statisticians have measured the quantitative effects of these factors upon the consumption of most foods and other goods derived from farm products.[1]

Table 4

Beef: Retail Price per Pound, Per Capita Consumption, and Per Capita Disposable Personal Income, United States, 1947-1957

Year	Retail Price of Beef [1]	Per Capita Consumption of beef [2]	Per Capita Disposable Income
	Cents	Lb.	$
	P	C	I
1947	61.8	69.6	1,181
1948	75.3	63.1	1,291
1949	68.4	63.9	1,271
1950	75.4	63.4	1,369
1951	88.2	56.1	1,473
1952	86.6	62.2	1,520
1953	69.1	77.6	1,582
1954	68.5	80.1	1,582
1955	67.5	82.0	1,660
1956	66.0	85.4	1,727
1957	70.6	84.5	1,782

[1] Choice grade.
[2] Civilian consumption.

Take a simple example: consumer demand for beef in the period 1947 through 1957. Table 4 summarizes the data on retail price, per capita consumption, and per capita income. In a general way, you can see from the table that per capita beef consumption varies *inversely* with retail price (that is, beef consumption tends to be high when price is low, and vice versa), and *directly* with income (that is, beef consumption tends to be high when per capita income is high, and vice versa). The statistician tries to pin down such general, vague

---

[1] Frederick L. Thompson and Richard J. Foote, *Agricultural Prices.* New York: McGraw-Hill Book Co., Inc., 1952, 2nd ed.

Warren C. Waite and Harry C. Trelogan, *Agricultural Market Prices.* New York: John Wiley & Sons, Inc., 1951, 2nd ed.

Karl A. Fox, *The Analysis of Demand for Farm Products.* Technical Bulletin No. 1081, U. S. Department of Agriculture, 1953.

observations. He wants to know *how much* beef consumption goes up when the price drops five cents a pound, or when per capita income goes up $200.

We shall not discuss the method in any detail. But the general nature of the results can be shown either in the form of a diagram or in the form of a numerical equation. The appropriate diagram is Figure 5. It is divided into three parts. The top part relates beef consumption to retail price. Each dot on this part of the chart shows both the retail price and the associated per capita consumption. Thus, the dot labeled 47 indicates that in 1947 the average retail price of beef was 61.8 cents a pound and that per capita consumption was 69.6 pounds.

Any competent statistician would note two facts at this point: *first,* that there is a general tendency for beef consumption to be relatively high when prices are relatively low, but, *second,* that changes in consumer income obscure the relationship somewhat—for example, higher incomes in the period 1953-1957 resulted in higher consumption than in 1949, when price was about the same. The line drawn through the dots in the top part of Figure 5 is intended as *an estimate of how consumption of beef would have varied with changes in retail price if consumer income had been held constant at the average of the period.*

In other words, this line is an estimate of the *demand curve.* We shall come back to this matter in a moment. First, let us consider the rest of the information shown in Figure 5.

The middle part of the diagram shows how consumer income was related to beef consumption—or, more precisely, how it was related to those variations in beef consumption that were not already accounted for by the demand curve at the top of the chart. For example, the dot labeled 47 in the mid-section of Figure 5 shows that per capita disposable income in 1947 was $1,181 and that per capita beef consumption was *11.7 pounds below the level indicated on the demand curve.* The dots in the middle of the diagram obviously line up very closely around the smooth curve we have drawn through them. This sort of curve is often called an Engels curve, after Friedrich Engels, one of the first statisticians to

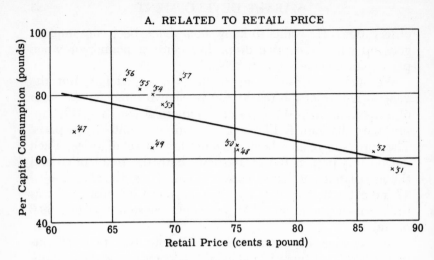

A. RELATED TO RETAIL PRICE

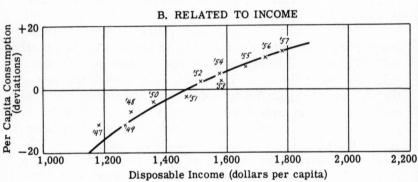

B. RELATED TO INCOME

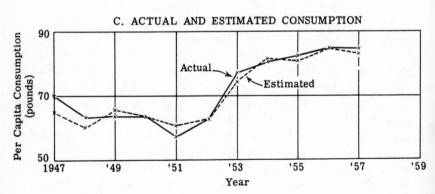

C. ACTUAL AND ESTIMATED CONSUMPTION

Figure 5.   Consumer Demand for Beef in the United States, 1947 through 1957.

94

make quantitative measurements of the relationship between consumer income and the consumption of various goods and services.

Finally, the bottom grid of Figure 5 shows the actual per capital consumption of beef from 1947 through 1957 and compares it with the consumption levels that could be estimated from the demand curve and the Engels curve, if price and income were known. For example, the upper part of the chart shows that in 1947 retail price alone would suggest a beef consumption of 80.0 pounds; the middle part shows that the income of that year would reduce this estimate by 14.8 pounds. So our estimate would be 80.0 minus 14.8 = 65.2 pounds. Actual consumption was 69.6 pounds. The error in 1947 was 4.4 pounds—higher than that for any other year. In general, you can see that the two factors, price and income, explain most of the variation in beef consumption during the period in question.

So far, we have used graphic analysis only. Some statisticians prefer to compute an estimating equation. Neglecting the known curvature in the Engels function, and assuming linear relations throughout, a least-squares equation relating

$\bar{c}$, representing the estimate of beef consumption, to

p, representing the retail price of beef, and

i, representing per capita income,

is

$$\bar{c} = 74.98 - 0.845p + 0.0388i$$

This equation summarizes essentially the same information as that portrayed by the demand curve and the Engels curve in Figure 5, except, of course, that it assumes that both are straight lines. To estimate beef consumption from the equation, we would simply insert the appropriate price and income data and compute $\bar{c}$. Thus, in 1957 the price was $p_{57} = 70.6$ and the income was $i_{57} = \$1,782$, so that the estimated per capita consumption in 1957 would be:

$$\bar{c} = 74.98 - (0.845)(70.6) + (0.0388)(1782)$$
$$= 84.46 \text{ pounds.}$$

The actual consumption was 84.5 pounds, so that the estimate was within the limits of error of the data.

The demand equation, like the chart in Figure 5, is intended only to illustrate the general nature of demand curves and Engels curves. We use this particular example of beef consumption because it happens to be simple and easy to explain. Actually, economic life is usually complicated. You may well wonder whether the demand for beef is not influenced by additional factors such as the supply and price of pork. Also, if you have had a good course in statistics, you should realize that the rising demand for beef in this period could have been attributed to a time trend rather than to income. Such criticisms are valid and important even though the multiple correlation in this case was 0.99, and even though the numbers in the estimated equation are highly significant according to the usual mathematical tests.

Demand Curves and Engels Curves

Figure 5 should help you understand the meaning of a demand curve or an Engels curve. When the economist talks about the demand for beef he is talking about the whole demand curve. The same thing is true of any other commodity. The demand for potatoes is a statement of what quantities of potatoes consumers would buy at various stated retail prices. Thus, the demand for any commodity can be described by a curve on a diagram or by an equation.

When the economist says that the demand for some commodity has increased, he doesn't necessarily mean that the consumption of that commodity has increased. Rather, he means that the whole demand curve is higher than it used to be. If he says that the demand for milk is higher than it was last year, he means that consumers would be willing to buy more at the old price or that they would be willing to pay a higher price for the same quantity they used to buy. In a similar way, the whole Engels curve may shift upward or downward over a period of time; that is, consumers with a given income may be willing to buy more of the commodity now than they would have bought at some time in the past with the same income. It is important to keep these ideas clearly in mind when analyzing marketing problems. This is especially true when thinking about problems of advertising, promotion, and market development. The purpose of all such programs is to change the demand for some commodity or services. More specifically, the usual purpose is to raise demand—that is, to raise the whole demand curve so that either more will be bought at the old price or a higher price will be paid for the same quantity. In some cases, the purpose may be to change the slope of the demand curve to make it either steeper or flatter.

Elasticity

Economists often speak about "the elasticity of demand." More particularly, they are concerned with at least two different kinds of elasticity—sometimes called "price elasticity" and "income elasticity." You can no doubt be happy and can do perfectly good marketing research without knowing all the mathematical refinements concerning elasticity. But you certainly should know whether a given demand curve (or a given Engels curve) is elastic or inelastic. Marketing policies that are profitable when demand is inelastic may be quite unprofitable when demand is elastic.

A Frenchman, Augustin Cournot,[2] originated the distinction between elastic and inelastic demand curves (although he did not use the words "elastic" and "inelastic," which are due to Marshall).[3] He was concerned specifically with price elasticity. He would define an elastic demand as one in which a slight lowering of prices would expand consumption so much that consumers would spend more money for a commodity; if consumption would expand only a little, so that consumers would spend less, demand would be inelastic.

Suppose we try this on our beef example. In the period studied, the average price of beef was 72.491 cents a pound, and average consumption was 71.627 pounds per capita. This meant a per capita expenditure of $51.92. What would have

---

[2] Augustin Cournot, *Mathematical Principles of the Theory of Wealth*. Translated by N. T. Bacon. New York: The Macmillan Company, 1929, pp. 47-48.
[3] Alfred Marshall, *Principles of Economics*. New York: The Macmillan Company, 1936, Ch. 4.

happened if the average price of beef had been, say, 5 cents a pound lower? Our estimating equation indicates that consumption would have gone up by (0.845) (5) = 4.225 pounds, so it would have been 71.627 + 4.225 = 75.852 pounds. The average consumer would have spent (75.852) (0.67491) = $51.19 for beef. This is slightly *less* than he actually spent at the higher price, so the indication is that the demand for beef is slightly *inelastic*. (You might try making similar estimates from the curve in the top grid of Figure 5.)

Cournot did not discuss income-elasticity of demand. But an Engels curve is elastic if an increase in income induces consumers to spend a larger proportion of their income for the commodity in question—and, naturally, it is inelastic if consumers spend a smaller proportion.

In our beef example, consumers actually spent $51.92 out of an actual income of $1,494. This was 3.475 per cent of their income. Now, suppose income had been, say, $100 more. The demand equation estimates that they would have bought (0.0388) (100) = 3.88 pounds more of beef, making a total of 71.627 + 3.88 = 75.50 pounds. At 72.49 cents a pound, they would have spent $54.73 for beef. This would have been 3.434 per cent of their income—slightly *less* than before. So the indication is that the Engels curve is also slightly *inelastic*.

This sort of computation is enough for most practical purposes, but it will not give you a "coefficient of elasticity." An exact definition of such a coefficient requires an understanding of differential calculus.[4] But a very good approximation is this: the elasticity of y with respect to x is the expected percentage change in y that would be associated with a change of 1 per cent in x.

Our estimating formula indicates that a 1 per cent drop in price (that is, a drop of 0.72491 cents) would have increased the consumption of beef by 0.61255 pounds, or 0.855 per cent.

---

[4] If y is a function of x, the elasticity of y with respect to x is

$$e_{y \cdot x} = \frac{\partial y}{\partial x} \frac{x}{y}.$$

This definition is valid for all kinds of variables, not just for so-called "price elasticity" and "income elasticity."

For all practical purposes, the coefficient of price elasticity in this case is — 0.855, measured at the point where price and income were both at the average for the period.

Similarly, an increase of 1 per cent, or $14.944 in per capita income, would have raised beef consumption by 0.57833 pounds, or 0.807 per cent.

We repeat that these coefficients, — 0.855 and + 0.807, are not very important. The fact that — 0.855 is close to — 1.000 means that the demand curve is slightly inelastic—which we already knew. Similarly the fact that + 0.807 is close to + 1.000 means that the Engels curve also is slightly inelastic—which we also knew.

Ordinarily, all the marketing man needs to know is whether demand is elastic or inelastic. The exact coefficients are of little practical use. In recent years, statisticians have made estimates of the price elasticities and the income elasticities of most important farm products.[5] The main value of these estimates is to classify commodities into two groups: elastic and inelastic. This classification is very important to marketers, for the reasons pointed out by Cournot over a century ago.

Derived Demand

Naturally, when speaking of consumer demand, we think in terms of retail prices paid by the consumer. But the farmer does not get the retail price. Rather, he gets a much lower price, which is essentially the retail price minus all the charges for transportation, storage, processing, and distribution. Also, the processor and food manufacturer get less than the retail price, for obvious reasons. The farmer and the middleman are interested in "derived demand"—that is, in the demand for their commodities in terms of the prices they receive. For example, if we have a good estimate of the consumer demand curve and also know the costs and margins between the farmer and the consumer, we can obtain prices at the farm level by subtracting processing and marketing

---

[5] T. W. Schultz, *The Economic Organization of Agriculture*. New York: Mc-Graw-Hill Book Company, Inc, 1953, Ch. 5.

costs from the retail prices. This gives us an estimate of the derived demand at the farm level or whatever other level is of interest.

In actual statistical work, the economist often starts with the demand at the farm level rather than with consumer demand. There have been many arguments as to whether some of these statistical curves are really demand curves. As far as we are concerned, this is a rather unimportant matter which can be defined to suit one's own convenience. Statisticians have come to use the term "supply-price" curve when describing a curve relating the quantity of a farm product sold to the price received by farmers or by wholesalers.

An important fact about supply-price curves at the farm level is that they nearly always are less elastic (or, rather, more inelastic) than are the consumer demand curves. This is so because many of the charges for marketing and distribution are practically fixed, not changing much, if at all, when prices change. Freight rates are a typical example.

Making Use of Demand Elasticity

The elasticity of demand varies among products. There are some products, for example, the sales volume of which continues about the same irrespective of minor price changes. Demand is inelastic. The volume for other products, on the other hand, may be quite sensitive to price changes, in which case the demand is elastic.

If a concern is selling a product for which there is an elastic demand, this will mean that, the more it can sell of this product by reducing prices, the greater will be the total revenue from sales, provided that demand remains elastic. If, however, there is an inelastic demand for the product, revenue may be increased by raising the prices and selling less. This manipulation of quantity and price in relation to the price elasticity of demand would be an invaluable market tool for a group or concern with control over supply and price. Then it would be possible to calculate that combination of sales and prices which would increase income.

Market Analysis

A successful salesman will study a market before pricing or distributing his product. Sellers of agricultural products are no exception. The most fundamental information about a market concerns the behavior of consumers. How much of this product are consumers buying? When would they turn to substitutes if prices were raised? What is the potential for increased demand, and what are the expectations for increased income? These are some of the questions to be answered. A consideration of consumer behavior is by no means limited to price response. Such factors as income, social background, the actions of friends or neighbors, and many other psychological influences affect the purchase patterns of consumers. Students of markets are continually attempting to bring these factors to measurable proportions so that prediction of how consumers react to given market changes will provide useful guides to sellers.

Advertising and Promotion

Effective selling involves more than mere market analysis. It involves action to make the most of market opportunities. One line of action is to adjust production to the existing demand. Another course is to seek to manipulate demand through advertising and promotion.

Advertising has been a highly controversial topic for many years. It can be looked at from several viewpoints: that of individual sellers; that of a whole industry; that of society generally. We shall have something to say regarding each of these viewpoints. But first let us attempt some classification of different types of advertising and promotion according to their objectives, stated in economic terms.

The term "advertise" originally meant "to give notice." A great deal of modern advertising still is essentially informative in character—an effort to call attention of prospective customers to what one has to sell. Newspaper want ads are predominantly of this type.

But a very large and conspicuous part of advertising and promotion is designed not merely to inform but to persuade. In economic terms, such promotion is designed to change demand favorably to the product or brand that is advertised. Merely informative advertising, by contrast, is designed not to alter demand, but to make it effective by letting those who are in the market for products know where what they want can be obtained.

No hard-and-fast line can be drawn, to be sure, between promotions of the two types. But the contrast is marked between a Thursday night grocery ad listing details of Friday's bargains and a two-page color spread devoted to the thought that a particular model of automobile is the "most spirited." There is similar contrast between the hardware store clerk who helps you find the size nuts and bolts you want and the high-pressure salesman who seeks you out to exert his training in sales psychology in behalf of a product you didn't know you needed.

Promotion by Individual Firm

From the standpoint of the individual firm, whether to advertise and what type of advertising to use depend upon the type of product to be sold and the type of market it has. An individual wheat farmer has nothing to gain from advertising. Wheat is a standardized commodity, sold in a highly organized market with uniform prices for the different types and grades. There is always a market for his wheat; he has no need to announce its availability. And he can hardly hope to persuade buyers of its superiority to other wheats of the same quality.

To the seller of a less standardized product, or in a less well organized market, advertising may be profitable or even essential. Mail-order firms obviously must distribute catalogs to get business. Pine Croft Nursery may substantially increase its sales by local ads reminding householders that the season for planting evergreens is at hand, and by urging that it has an unusually fine stock from which to select.

Consumers are known to drive many miles to buy at a particular orchard that has by advertising built up a reputation for fine apples, even though the established market grade standards·

would recognize no difference between these apples and those from many other orchards.

Such a seller has modified the demand in favor of his product, and in so doing has gained a competitive advantage in the market. His ability to do so depends upon the possibility of "differentiating" his product—or himself as an exceptional supplier of it. The result is both to increase the demand for it and to make the demand inelastic, in the sense that buyers will be reluctant to substitute other brands for it. Advertising thus enables him to sell more of the product and to charge a higher price for it. How far he can press this advantage is limited, of course, by the availability of similar products and by consumers' awareness that satisfactory substitutes are available.

PROMOTIONAL COMPETITION

Successful advertising by competitors may force a firm to spend money advertising its own brand simply to hang onto its share of the market. When advertising is thus competitive, its chief effect may be to make the demand for each competing *brand* of a product more inelastic without appreciably increasing *total demand for all brands* of the commodity.

To the extent that this occurs, each seller may be able to charge a somewhat higher price for his product than he otherwise could. So long as the demand for his brand is inelastic, he has no incentive to reduce the price; to do so would not increase sales enough to make up for the lower price. Competition is transferred from the arena of price to the arena of promotion.

Such a situation has obvious implications regarding the difficulties that face a new firm. It may find considerable promotional expenditure necessary in order to draw enough customers away from the established suppliers to give it a foothold in the market.

INNOVATIONS

"Demand creation" through promotion has a special role in the case of innovations. A firm offering a new product or a new service must obviously take steps to call buyers' attention to it. But if the product is really of a new kind, the firm must do more than this. It must educate prospective buyers to the uses of the product—make them aware, not just of its existence, but of what it is good for—and persuade them that it is really something they have always wanted and needed. Literally, it must create a demand where none existed before.

Promotion of innovations is inherently risky. Buyers may take to the new product or they may not. Yet constant innovation is a vital characteristic of our progressive, technological society. Our economic growth and rising levels of living have consisted not so much of just having more and more of the same goods and services as of having a continuous flow of new products and of improvements in products. We have come to take this sort of change for granted. We are receptive to innovation.

Hence, a great deal of effort by many firms goes into product innovation. This is true of foods and other agricultural commodities as well as of automobiles and appliances and other mechanical gadgets. There is a constant stream of new food products, new wrappings, new sizes, pre-washing, pre-peeling, pre-cooking, and other convenience features.

And a great deal of competitive promotion is based upon exploiting consumers' interest in innovation. Established products, as well as new ones, seek recurrently to achieve the appearance of innovation in order to keep attention. Promotion must say, in effect, "the same good product you have loved so long, only better."

GUIDES TO POLICY

What economic principles should guide a firm's policy on promotion? Obviously, the law of diminishing returns applies. Beyond some point, additional expenditures on promotion bring decreasing returns. The problem is to identify this point.

The basic principle is easy to state, though it may be hard to apply: For a promotional expenditure to be profitable, the added net revenue that results—either from larger sales or from higher prices or from both—must be greater than the cost of the promotion. The problem, of course, turns on forecasting what the added net revenue will be.

Since the profit from promotion turns upon added *net* revenue, the firm's production cost structure enters the calculation. If it is producing at rising marginal cost, added sales will bring decreasing additions to net revenue. This places a limitation on the amount of promotional expenditure that will pay.

If, on the other hand, the firm is producing at decreasing marginal cost, sales expansion will bring increasing additions to net revenue. In the case of product innovations, this is particularly likely to be true. Producers of new products are under great pressure to build sales rapidly past the "break-even point."

To take advantage of mass-production techniques requires the development of mass markets for the products. Firms in such industries have an incentive to attempt through advertising to mold consumers nationally to acceptance of the mass-produced products. This means the rooting out of local tastes and individual preferences. In such a market, however, some smaller firms may nevertheless compete by catering to the tastes of local consumers willing a pay a little more to satisfy their individual preferences. Small bakeries that do a successful local business in specialty breads and pastries are an example.

MULTIPLE-LINE BRANDS

Economy of scale applies to promotional expenditure itself. A successfully established brand name can be extended to a variety of products. The cost of promoting the *name* is thus distributed over a number of items. This is one reason for multiple-line processors in the food industries—companies like Heinz with its "fifty-seven varieties."

MANUFACTURERS VERSUS DISTRIBUTORS

Food manufacturers do not sell directly to the consumers who use their products. Sale to consumers is in the hands of retail distributors. Many manufacturers do not put their own brand on products, but pack them under the labels of the distributors to whom they are sold.

If a manufacturer decides to maintain his own brand, however, he must seek through promotion to create the kind of consumer demand that will persuade retailers to stock his products. The promotional program is also beamed directly at the distributors, of course, and often involves special allowances to them for featuring the company's products in the store and in store advertising. This includes such gimmicks as recurrent give-aways, tie-in sales, coupon offers, and so forth.

PROMOTION BY RETAILERS

These gimmicks are one means of reconciling the conflict of interest between the brand manufacturer and the retailer. The problem of the retailer is to build a large and steady volume of sales for his store as a whole. He has no direct interest in promoting the sale of one product or brand in preference to another—unless it be his own private brand. Hence, store advertising and promotion are directed, with varying relative emphasis, toward creating in the housewife's mind an image of the store as an economical place to buy yet offering the utmost in convenience, elegance, friendliness, and polite service.

PRICE "LEADERS"

Food-store advertising typically features "leaders" at reduced prices designed to attract customers to the store—in the expectation that, once in, they will purchase the other things they need. Brand proprietors are fearful of use of their products as leaders lest through competition among stores the "feature" prices become the prevailing prices, with resulting pressure to reduce the manufacturer's price. Hence their sponsorship of one-time-only store features, over which they can maintain some control and that can be tied in with their over-all promotional programs.

Promotion by the Industry

We have noted in passing that intense promotional competition among firms may be of little benefit from the standpoint of the industry—that is, of the firms collectively—if its chief effect is upon division of sales among brands rather than to increase total sales of the industry's product. There is a common presumption that the attention called to the product by brand promotion does increase total sales, and this is likely the case in varying degree. There is competition between industries, just as between brands, that may impose a similar necessity for competitive promotion. Even if brand promotions do increase industry sales, however—or maintain them in the face of competition from other industries—it need not follow that this is the most economical means of doing so from an industry standpoint.

PROMOTION AND PRICE COMPETITION

If the demand for an industry's product is elastic, the industry collectively would usually be better off to lower its price and spend less on advertising. Yet, as we have seen, this is unlikely to occur under promotional competition. The firms in the industry have little incentive individually to substitute a price reduction for promotion. Each is fearful that his competitors would match the price reduction and he would find himself in the same promotional battle as before but at a lower price level.

COMMODITY PROMOTIONS

Advertising and promotion by industry associations—as distinct from individual firms—have developed in recent years in a number of farm products. The American Dairy Association with its nationwide promotion of milk drinking; the National Cotton Council; apple, citrus, and other fruit-producer groups; and the beef and lamb industries are examples. Some promotions are carried on by large producers' co-operatives, like Sunkist. Some are sponsored by governmental agencies, especially at the state level, under laws that impose a tax on sales to provide funds for promotion. The Federal government helps organize promotions for particular commodities at times when they are in surplus supply.

Commodity promotions have two aims. One aim is to increase current demand for seasonal products as they come on the market, so that better prices can be obtained for them. Such promotion may combine general advertising with co-operative arrangements with retail distributors to promote the commodity, much after the manner of brand promotions.

LONG-RANGE PROMOTION

Much commodity promotion, however, aims at longer-range increase of demand for the commodity by shifting consumer preferences in its favor. Promotion of milk drinking, of beef eating, or of taking lemon juice before breakfast as a laxative is of this character.

The effectiveness of such promotions is difficult to assess. Citrus advertising is an example of apparent success. Fifty years ago, oranges were something put in children's stockings at Christmas as a special treat. Today orange juice is regarded by millions of families as a daily dietary necessity. Nutritional education of the public has at least provided a favorable climate for successful promotion of citrus fruits. Meanwhile, broilers are an example of a commodity that has greatly increased in consumption without the benefit of industry advertising.

COMMODITY VERSUS BRAND PROMOTION

One economic contrast of industry with firm promotions should be mentioned. As previously pointed out, one promotional aim of the individual firm is to build customer loyalty —in economic terms, to make the demand for its brand less elastic. In agricultural industries, however, afflicted as they are with fluctuations in supply due to weather and other causes difficult to control, it would appear logical to seek to make demand *more* elastic, so that large supplies can be moved into consumption with less drop in price. (It may also be an aim, however, to make demand less responsive to changes in prices of competing commodities.)

Viewed in this light, the promotional aims of farm producer groups (unless they are in a position collectively to regulate supplies or prices) would appear to be more closely aligned with those of distributors than of processors. For distributors are interested in featuring bargains in individual commodities to attract customers to their stores. Their advertising emphasizes prices and thus encourages consumer price consciousness. Processors, on the other hand, tend quite understandably to prefer stable volume at stable prices, and are fearful of involvement in price competition.

Social Aspects of Promotion

What is the role of advertising and promotion viewed from the standpoint of the agricultural marketing system as a whole? Do they help or hinder making the best use of productive resources in fulfilling consumers' needs and wants? These questions have been hotly argued for many years. They continue to be controversial. We can hardly settle them here, but we offer some observations and comments that we consider apropos.

ADVERTISING AS COMMUNICATIONS

First of all, let us point out again what a large and complex job is involved in marketing agricultural commodities in the United States. Such an operation requires an elaborate system of communications. This is peculiarly important in our kind of economy, that works primarily through the independent decisions of private individuals rather than by central direction. To make wise decisions, the individuals must be well informed, and this poses a great problem in communications.

It is consistent with the general pattern of our society that we depend for communications, as for other activities, largely upon private initiative. Advertising and other promotional endeavors are one of the chief forms that privately sponsored communications take.

COSTLINESS OF PROMOTION

To meet the informational needs of a market such as ours is inevitably costly. This is a matter that many devotees of perfect competition seem to overlook. They neglect to take account of the costs of providing all buyers and sellers with full and adequate information, although this is one of the requisites of the perfect market. Dependence upon privately sponsored advertising for communications is one way of getting the job paid for.

The job is becoming increasingly costly. Advertising and promotion expenditures have for many years been going up at a more rapid rate than gross national product. This means that we are devoting to them an increasing proportion of the nation's productive resources.

Advertising and promotion have inherent shortcomings as a market communications system; we shall point to some of them. But constructive criticism must appraise the job, not just in relation to an abstract ideal, but in relation to realistic ways of doing it better or more cheaply.

INFORMATIVE PROMOTION

Let us first return to our distinction between the advertising and promotion which are essentially informative and those which are primarily persuasive. Few would deny the constructive role of informative advertising. The main complaints are that it cannot be relied upon to give all the relevant facts and that it may at times present facts in misleading ways or even give misinformation. This is an inherent shortcoming; those who pay the bill can be expected to dictate the message.

This shortcoming is at least partly self-corrective, however. An advertiser knows that he can be effective only to the extent that those whom he addresses rely upon what he says. This self-correction process is helped if buyers have other channels of information providing facts that they can use to check up on advertising matter. Over time, self-interest will lead advertisers who wish to stay in business to eschew apparent misinformation, and competition will lead them to provide the kinds of information that their audience wants.

Meanwhile, private communication is and should be supplemented by public information such as market news services. Opportunity for misrepresentation is reduced by such things as grade standards, which provide a language of communication not easily susceptible to misleading use. Ethical standards are supported by trade practices of advertising media in refusing to publish misleading ads, and by laws penalizing those found guilty of misrepresentation. Comparison of present-day advertising with that of fifty years ago suggests progress both in truthfulness and in the adequacy of information presented.

PERSUASIVE PROMOTION

But what of the persuasive element in promotion? Here is

where the hottest controversy rages. Advertising and promotion are accused of preaching false values, of corrupting public tastes and morals, and of doing these things, not openly and aboveboard, but in reprehensibly subtle and insinuating ways that the victim cannot detect and that thus leave him helpless in the hands of his exploiters.

All of us are aware of the continual sales pressure to buy this and buy that. Demand stimulation and demand maintenance have become an accepted part of the American scene. And, as we have seen, competitive pressures between firms and between industries make this a process that feeds upon itself and grows.

ADVERTISING AND ECONOMIC GROWTH

Again, it would seem an inherent characteristic of private advertising and promotion that they will use communications for persuasion. This is not necessarily wholly objectionable. Defenders of advertising argue that its persuasive effects are a chief contributor to the economic progress of which we boast. The potential benefits of technological advance can be realized only as demand for new products is created by public persuasion.

ADVERTISING AND HEALTH

Part of the argument turns on the matter of tastes and moral preferences. In the case of foods, for example, or of cigarettes, it is complained that there is no assurance that the kinds of consumption promoted are those most conducive to good nutrition and health. Many examples of such shortcomings can be cited. But a great deal of food advertising does feature claims of nutritional benefit. And in a democracy, who but the people themselves are to decide whether to live to eat or to eat to live? There is some evidence that the nutritional status of the population has improved over the past generation or two, and there is some reason to believe that advances in nutritional science have been a factor in this, and that advertising has helped draw public attention to advances in our knowledge of nutrition.

Here, again, one obvious corrective to false information is an adequate flow of information and opinion through other channels, that can criticize advertising and present opposing sets of values, to keep before people the choices they are making and the possible consequences.

PSYCHOLOGY AND PROMOTION

The charge that modern promotion uses "unfair" methods of persuasion raises issues of a different sort. To be sure, persuasion, in salesmanship and courtship, has always been a game of wits, in which part of the skill lies in keeping the opponent unaware of the arts that are being practiced upon him. Modern psychology, however, is increasingly transforming these arts into a science, and the scientific manipulation of men's minds and emotions opens powers capable of great mischief. This problem goes far beyond the realm of economics.

This dilemma strikes at the roots of theories of political economy that assume that the free choices of consumers should be the ultimate criteria in economics. What becomes of freedom of choice when choice-making is manipulated? The hope must be, again, that, through open channels of information, consumers can be armed for defense and kept no more than one step behind those who are devising new techniques of persuasion.

HOW MUCH FOR PROMOTION?

Meanwhile, the economist is left to ponder the problem of how large a proportion of our productive resources can, in the name of economic development or otherwise, be advantageously devoted to persuading ourselves to "higher" standards of living.

QUESTIONS FOR DISCUSSION

1. Explain elasticity of demand (a) with respect to income, and (b) with respect to price. The demand for cereal products and potatoes is very inelastic. The demand for beef and for strawberries is much more elastic. Why is this so?

2. How does consumption respond to changes in consumer income? To changes in retail prices?

3. Outline a program promoting a good product for a processor with a limited budget.

4. How much promotion is enough? What is the value of this activity to the economy?

SUPPLEMENTARY READING

1. Barger, Harold, *Distribution's Place in the American Economy Since 1869*. New York: National Bureau of Economic Research, Inc., 1955, pp. 28-36.
2. Borden, Neil H., *The Economic Effects of Advertising*. Homewood, Ill.: Richard D. Irwin, 1942, Ch. 6.
3. Vaile, Grether, and Cox, *Marketing in the American Economy*. New York: Ronald Press Company, 1952, Ch. 13.
4. Waite, Warren C., and Harry C. Trelogan, *Agricultural Market Prices*. New York: John Wiley & Sons, Inc., 2nd ed., 1951, Ch. 3, pp. 35-58.
5. Waugh, Frederick V., ed., *Readings on Agricultural Marketing*. Ames: Iowa State College Press, 1954, Ch. 2, pp. 27-108.

10

The Principles of Market Allocation

The next four chapters will discuss some of the key decisions in the marketing of farm products: (1) *where* to buy and sell, (2) *when* to buy and sell, (3) *in what form* to buy and sell, and (4) *from whom* to buy and *to whom* to sell.

The answers to all of these key problems depend upon the same general principle. The buyer or seller of farm products must understand this principle if he is to make a profit. The student of agricultural marketing must understand the principle if he is to know what is going on in the world, and especially if he is to help find improvements.

Before going further, we would like to make it very clear that the coming four chapters are not concerned with the amounts of farm products produced. They are concerned solely with the distribution of a crop after it has been produced. This is the typical problem in agricultural marketing. The man who markets the crop ordinarily has little or no control over supply. Even if he is a farmer, the market supply is usually determined for him. His marketing job is to find the best way to sell whatever quantity he has. This is even truer of the marketing job of big concerns like meat packers, milk distributors, and tobacco companies. They buy whatever is produced, but they ordinarily have a good deal to say about how it is to be distributed—that is, how it is allocated among various segments of the market.

In each of these chapters we shall discuss a problem from two different points of view—first that of perfect competition, and, second, that of imperfect competition.

In the case of perfect competition the decisions made by a buyer or a seller have no measurable effect upon market prices.

For example, suppose a farmer has a thousand bushels of wheat to sell. Whatever he decides to do with it, his effect upon market prices will be so small that it would take a high-powered microscope to see it on a chart. When a man is buying or selling in a perfectly competitive market (that is, where his actions have no effect upon market prices), his most profitable course is to buy his entire supply in whatever part of the market offers it at the lowest net price and to sell his entire supply to whatever part of the market offers him the highest net price. In this connection, "net price" means the market price minus all costs such as transportation, storage, and processing.

But the very process of each individual selling in whatever part of the market offers the highest net price must result rather quickly in an equilibrium in which net prices tend to be the same in all parts of the market. Clark and Weld [1] describe this as a process of "equalization." They say that equalization is perhaps the most important function of wholesale markets. They obviously have in mind the equalization of net prices in all parts of the market.

Under perfect competition such equalization of net prices would be inevitable. It is sometimes assumed that such equalization is also "best" or "optimum" in the sense that it is more beneficial to the general public than any other set-up of prices. We shall not discuss this matter in any detail in the coming four chapters. It is briefly mentioned on pages 55 to 60. In general, the coming four chapters will be concerned with profitable methods of marketing rather than with morals or with any particular concept of the public welfare. We suggest that the student keep an open mind on these matters until he has finished the four chapters.

When buying or selling in markets where competition is imperfect (so that a man's decisions do affect market prices), his most profitable course of action usually is not to sell his entire crop in that part of the market that offers the highest net price. Rather, it is to allocate just enough to each part

---

[1] F. E. Clark and L. D. H. Weld, *Marketing Agricultural Products*. New York: The Macmillan Co., 1947.

of the market so that the net marginal returns are the same in each.

Figure 6 is intended to clarify the general principle discussed above. The two diagrams at the top of the chart show the assumed demand curves in market 1 and market 2 (or two segments of the total market). We are trying to illustrate a general principle here—not to find an answer to a particular, practical problem. The demand curves may represent any farm product. The two parts of the market may represent two geographical markets like New York and Chicago; two temporal markets like the market for apples in the fall and in the spring; markets for two forms of a commodity, such as the market for fresh oranges and for frozen orange juice; demands for food by high-income families and by low-income families.

Whatever the practical problem, let us assume that 3,000 units of a commodity have been produced and are to be sold this year in markets 1 and 2. If they are sold under perfectly competitive conditions, the price will be $1.50. Two thousand five hundred units will go to market 1, and 500 units to market 2. The net returns from the crop will be $4,500.

If you are a small operator selling in markets 1 and 2, and if the net price in market 1 gets above $1.50, you had better sell your entire supply there.

Years ago some economists and marketing experts thought that this process of equalization maximized the returns from a crop of a given size. This is seldom, if ever, true. Perhaps the reason can be seen in the two diagrams in the middle part of Figure 6. These diagrams show the same data as those in the top of the chart. The only difference is that here we have multiplied quantity times price to show the net returns in markets 1 and 2 rather than net prices in these markets. Note that the maximum returns from market 1 occur when about 2,000 units are sold in that market, and that maximum returns from market 2 occur when about 1,350 units are sold there. Now, consider the case where 2,500 units are sold in market 1, and 500 units in market 2, both at the price of $1.50. The seller could get more from market 1 if he sold less there. But he could get more in market 2 if he sold more in that market. Thus, if he switches some of his sales from market 1

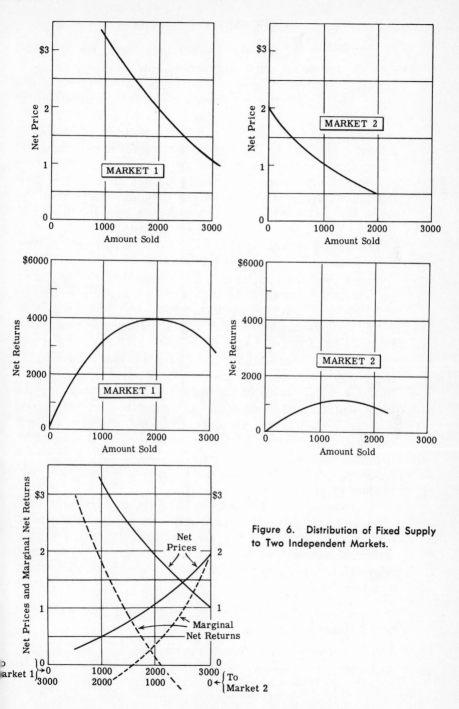

Figure 6. Distribution of Fixed Supply to Two Independent Markets.

117

to market 2, he will make a profit both ways. He can keep this up, switching more and more units from market 1 to market 2 until the slopes of the two net returns curves are equal. The slope in the net returns curve is the same thing as marginal net returns.

Perhaps the best way to analyze the problem of allocating a fixed supply to two segments of the market is that shown at the bottom of the chart. The two heavy curves show net prices in the two parts of the market. They are identical with the curves at the top part of the diagram except that the curve for market 2 has been reversed. The scale for the quantity sent to market 2 now reads from right to left.

The dotted curves on this diagram show marginal net returns from each segment of the market.

Under conditions of perfect competition the price would be set where the two demand curves cross one another; that is, at $1.50. As we have seen before, 2,500 units would go to market 1 and 2,500 units to market 2. The net income is measured by the area of the rectangle with 3,000 units as the base, and with $1.50 as the height. This area is obviously $4,500. On the other hand, the most profitable allocation of 3,000 units to these two segments of the market is found by noticing the point where the two marginal net returns curves cross one another. This indicates a shipment of 1,900 units to market 1 at a price of $2.05, and 1,100 units to market 2 at a price of $1. This gives a total income of $4,995, or $495 more than would be obtained by the competitive distribution of the same amount of goods.

We shall not linger to discuss all of the many ramifications of these rather difficult diagrams. It is well to get the general idea of them before reading the next four chapters. But after you finish reading the next four chapters, it would be a good idea to come back to this diagram and see if you understand it any better.

A Digression on Total, Average, and Marginal Payments and Returns

The analysis of any form of price discrimination, whether in buying or in selling, requires the use of such concepts as marginal payments and marginal returns. We discussed these concepts for discontinuous cases on pages 74 to 76. The careful student will want a more exact statement of principles applying to the general continuous case, where supply and consumption can change by very small amounts.

Those of you who are familiar with differential calculus should not have much trouble with these concepts. The mathematics can be summarized briefly as follows:

Supply

$$\text{supply price, } p = f(q)$$
$$\text{payments, } e = qp$$
$$\text{marginal payments} = \frac{de}{dq} = p + q\frac{dp}{dq}$$

Demand

$$\text{demand price, } P = F(Q)$$
$$\text{returns, } R = QP$$
$$\text{marginal returns} = \frac{dR}{dQ} = P + Q \cdot \frac{dP}{dQ}$$

Whether you understand differential calculus or not, the graphic principles can be understood by anyone who is willing to do a little work on it. The top part of Figure 7 shows how marginal payments are related to supply prices. The bottom part shows how marginal returns are related to demand prices. The graphics of marginal returns were explained in detail by Robinson.[2] The general idea can perhaps be expressed in words as follows. Suppose the quantity Q is being sold at price P so that the seller's returns are QP. What happens to his returns if he sells one unit more? He gets approximately the price P for the additional unit. But this additional unit will presumably drive down the demand price a little, at least. Suppose the price is reduced by δP. This involves a loss of δP for each of the Q units he sold before, or a loss of $Q \cdot \delta P$. But a unit can be of an arbitrary size. It might be a

---

[2] Joan Robinson, *The Economics of Imperfect Competition.* Macmillan and Co., Ltd., London, 1938.

pound, a bushel, a carload, or a shipload. If we imagine the unit to become smaller and smaller, we reach the definition of marginal returns in the mathematical sense of the differential calculus.

We leave it to the reader to make a similar interpretation of the top part of Figure 7 showing the relation between supply prices and marginal payments.

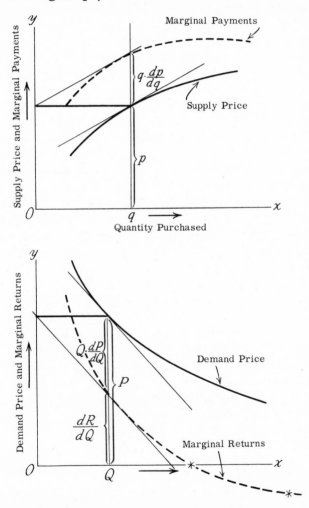

Figure 7.   Graphics of Marginal Payments and Returns.

Note that these diagrams show only how to locate a single point, either on the marginal payments curve or on the marginal returns curve. For example, if the demand curve is known, anyone can easily find the demand price that would correspond with any given quantity sold on the market. Draw a tangent to the demand curve at this point. Then draw a line from point P on the price axis parallel to the tangent to the demand curve. Note where this new line crosses the perpendicular drawn from point Q. The height of this intersection above the x-axis measures the marginal returns associated with the quantity Q. But obviously the same principle can be used to find any number of points on these curves. We have indicated several points by x's and have drawn the dotted curves through these points.

The same mathematics and the same curves apply to the principles of price discrimination, whether the discrimination is by place, by form, by time, or by persons. Thus, we will use the same mathematics and the same curves to analyze the problems in Chapters 11 through 14.

Marginal returns may be positive, negative, or zero. Positive marginal returns indicate that the total returns curve is rising —in other words, that demand is elastic. Negative marginal returns mean the opposite—that total returns are falling and that demand is inelastic.

In the practical cases in agriculture, at least, marginal payments are positive. We assume a positively sloping supply function in any part of the producing area. That is, we assume that if a buyer wants to purchase a larger quantity of a farm product from any area, he will have to pay a price that is at least somewhat higher. If he increases his purchases, say, 10 per cent from some area, and if he also has to pay prices at least somewhat higher, his payments to farmers will increase by more than 10 per cent. At least we assume that in all such cases his total payments curve will rise with increasing purchases. This means that his marginal payments to any area will be positive.

This may sound rather technical. Actually, we have tried to simplify the theory as much as possible without making it unrealistic. We are not interested here in displaying a lot of fancy mathematics and diagrams just for the fun of it. The concepts of marginal payments and of marginal returns are basic to an understanding of the principles of discriminatory pricing.

The idea is simply this. If marginal payments to area A are higher than those to area B, the buyer can always make a profit by buying one unit less from area A and one unit more from area B. In a similar manner, if marginal returns from market X are greater than the marginal returns from market Y, the seller can always make a profit by transferring one or more units from market Y to market X. Such profits are always possible, so long as the marginal returns in two or more parts of the market are unequal.

Many economists have been trained to think of elasticity coefficients rather than in terms of marginal payment and marginal returns. This is unfortunate. The concepts of marginal payments and marginal returns are not only easy to understand, they are also very easy to apply to practical problems of price discrimination, whether on a basis of place, time, form, or person. The concept of elasticity, on the other hand, is awkward, complicated, and very difficult to apply to a problem of this kind.

However, for those economists who are deeply immersed in elasticity coefficients, or for those who like to do things the hard way, we suggest the following:

If a given quantity is to be sold in two markets, the most profitable allocation is one that makes the marginal returns in the two markets equal. Thus if the marginal returns in markets one and two are r_1' and r_2', a necessary condition for the most profitable allocation is

$$r'_1 = r'_2$$

But in each market

$$r' = p \left(1 + \frac{1}{e} \right)$$

where p is the price and e the coefficient of elasticity. Thus, the necessary condition for the most profitable allocation can be written:

$$p_1 \left(1 + \frac{1}{e_1} \right) = p_2 \left(1 + \frac{1}{e_2} \right)$$

or

$$\frac{p_1}{p_2} = \frac{(1 + e_2) \, e_1}{(1 + e_1) \, e_2}$$

In other words, one must adjust the proportions of the supply sent to each market in such a way that the ratio of the prices in the two markets equals the complicated ratio to the right of the above equation.

Do not make the mistake of thinking that the most profitable allocation is one which results in equal elasticity in the two markets. This is never true under price discrimination where the prices in the two markets are unequal.

In this case, as in many other cases in economic theory, the elasticity coefficients are a nuisance.

QUESTIONS FOR DISCUSSION

1. What is meant by the process of price equalization?
2. Describe the most economical method a distributor should follow in allocating his sales between markets:
    (a) Assuming that his decisions do not affect market prices;
    (b) Assuming that his decisions do affect market prices.
3. How important are transportation costs in the location of markets under:
    (a) Perfect competition;
    (b) Imperfect competition.
4. How will the St. Lawrence Seaway affect farmers:
    (a) In the north central United States;
    (b) In the northeastern United States;
    (c) In France?
5. Define *net marginal returns*. What would be the economic significance of positive, zero, and negative net marginal returns in the market?
6. Give a nontechnical explanation either of the mathematical formula on page 119 for marginal returns or of the lower part of the diagram on page 120.

(*Hint:* if you are selling g units in a market and consider increasing to [g + 1] units,
your added income will be approximiately [1 × market price] plus [g × change in market price].) Why?

7. Explain in simple, nontechnical language how you can increase the income from selling a given quantity of a product in two markets by shifting part of the supply from one market to the other if the net marginal returns are not equal in the two markets. (*Hint:* Start by defining net marginal returns.)

SUPPLEMENTARY READING

1. Bain, Joe S., *Pricing, Distribution, and Employment.* New York: Henry Holt and Company, 1953, Ch. 9.
2. Clark, F. E., and L. D. H. Weld, *Marketing Agricultural Products in the United States.* New York: The Macmillan Company, 1932, p. 13.
3. Vaile, Grether, and Cox, *Marketing in the American Economy.* New York: Ronald Press Company, 1952, Part V.

11

Where to Buy and Sell

Suppose the buyer for Safeway Stores knows how many carloads of potatoes he needs delivered in New York City for the winter of 1959–1960. How many should he buy in Maine? In Michigan? In Idaho?

Or suppose that John Wyrowski, of Hadley, Massachusetts, plans to sell 200 truckloads of asparagus this spring. How many should he sell in Springfield? In Boston? In New York?

These are examples of typical marketing decisions. The man who usually makes the right (that is, the most profitable) decisions on matters of this kind is likely to be a successful marketer. The man who often buys or sells in the wrong place will not last long in the marketing business.

Buying Under Perfect Competition

Economists define perfect competition as a situation in which each buyer and seller has full and accurate information, where each operates independently, and where each is so small that his operations have no effects upon market prices. Remember this definition. We shall refer many times to perfect competition in Chapters 11 through 14.

Housewives buying lettuce illustrate the case of perfect competition. Most housewives buy one head of lettuce at a time. Few of them buy as many as 4 or 5 heads. Mrs. Taylor is not going to affect the price of lettuce, whether she buys it at her local store, goes to the supermarket in the big city, or drives out to a roadside stand in the country.

Independent buyers for small processors and distributors are in almost the same situation. Their purchases may affect the market a little. But unless they buy a significant proportion of the total supply in some area, their decisions are not likely to influence prices very much. They don't "make the market," but decide whether to accept or reject offers at the going prices. In such cases, competition is not technically perfect. But it is near enough to perfection so that the operator will not go far wrong if he follows the rules that are applicable strictly only to the case of perfect competition.

In situations characterized by perfect competition the rules are simple and clear: *buy wherever the total delivered cost (price plus freight, handling, and other expenses) is lowest,* assuming goods of identical quality.

Most buying of farm products follows this simple rule rather closely. Numerous examples can be seen every day—even in cases where economists would say that competition is not perfect. The feed manufacturer usually gets quotations on Number 3 yellow corn from several sources—and he usually will buy from whatever source can deliver it to him at the lowest cost. The buyer for the A & P is likely to switch from Maine potatoes to Michigan potatoes if he finds that Michigan can deliver potatoes of a comparable quality at a lower cost.

Thus, while the economist's definition of perfect competition is an abstract ideal that seldom occurs in the real world, much of the domestic business of agricultural marketing actually follows almost the same pattern that it would follow if competition were really perfect.

We shall come back to this after considering geographical aspects of selling under competition.

Selling Under Perfect Competition

Probably the most frequent economic advice is to "buy cheap and sell dear." We have said that under conditions of perfect competition each buyer would buy wherever his delivered costs were lowest. The reverse is that *each seller would sell where his net price (that is, price minus all charges for freight, handling, and so forth) is highest.*

The farmer selling hogs would get quotations from several markets, would subtract freight and other costs, and would sell wherever his net price was highest. The co-operative association selling oranges would quickly shift some cars from New York to Chicago if it got a higher net price from Chicago than from New York. And if the Liverpool price of wheat, minus freight and costs, were less than the domestic price in the United States, no U. S. wheat would be sold to Liverpool.

All this, of course, assumes perfect competition—including full and accurate information. This is a large order. We can never actually attain perfect competition, but many public policies are intended to encourage an approach toward it.

In an approximately competitive situation, the most successful operator is one that has the most recent, and most accurate, information on:

1. Prices received by sellers at country points;
2. Freight charges and other costs;
3. Prices paid by buyers in central and terminal markets.

Accurate, up-to-date market news is essential to the smooth working of competitive marketing. If the price rises in market A, greater supplies will be attracted there quickly and automatically. Wiener [1] overlooked this example of "cybernetics," that is, of automatic controls. A thermostat turns up the heat when the house gets cold—market news steps up supplies when prices are high.

"Equalization" of Prices

As Clark and Weld [2] pointed out, one of the main purposes of the central market is to "equalize" prices. All buyers of milk in Chicago—assuming perfect competition—would pay the same price delivered at Chicago. Each farmer shipping to Chicago would get the Chicago price less freight and handling costs. A dozen dairymen in the same town, 50 miles from Chicago would all get the same price. A dozen dairymen in another town 100 miles out would all get a lower price because the transportation cost is more. The wholesale price of

---

[1] Norbert Wiener, *Cybernetics*. Cambridge, Mass.: Technology Press, 1948.
[2] Fred E. Clark and L. D. H. Weld, *Marketing Farm Products*. New York: The Macmillan Company, 1947.

Georgia watermelons in Baltimore, New York, and St. Louis would be the price f.o.b. Georgia, plus freight and other costs to each of these cities.

Since transportation costs vary with distance, we would expect more or less regular geographical price patterns. Farmers near the principal consuming centers would get the highest prices. As you went further and further out from the big city, the farmer would get a lower and lower price.

Similarly, the delivered price in a city near the area of production would be low. This price would rise as the distance increased. If we knew the freight rates and other costs associated with distance, we could predict price differentials accurately—again assuming perfect competition.

These principles are rather well-known. They form the basis of most books on the economics of location.[3] Yet, they are often forgotten by those who should know better. If all dealers in a wholesale market pay the same price, someone may accuse them of monopoly, although we would expect the same result under perfect competition.

Several competent economists have found that geographical patterns of agricultural prices within the United States are usually very close to the patterns we would expect under perfect competition.

An especially simple and striking example is shown in Figure 8. The map at the top of Figure 8 is like a contour map of the United States. But instead of showing equal elevations above sea level, the irregular lines show equal milk prices to farmers. The lower map shows how these lines of equal prices would look if the price anywhere in the country had been $ (3.43 + .001353 x), where x is the distance in miles from Eau Claire, Wisconsin.

You can no doubt observe several discrepancies (differences) between the prices in the two maps. But the remarkable thing

---

[3] Edgar M. Hoover, *The Location of Economic Activity*. New York: McGraw-Hill Book Co., Inc., 1948.

August Lösch, *The Economics of Location*. New Haven: Yale University Press, 1954.

Alfred Weber, *Theory of the Location of Industries*. Carl J. Freidrich, ed. Chicago: University of Chicago Press, 1957.

ACTUAL EQUAL-PRICE LINES°

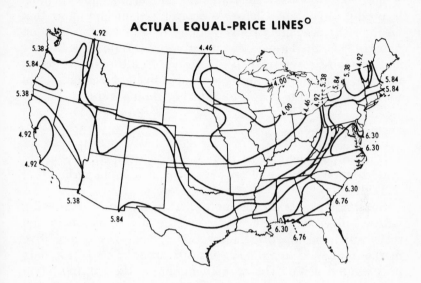

CALCULATED EQUAL-PRICE LINES△

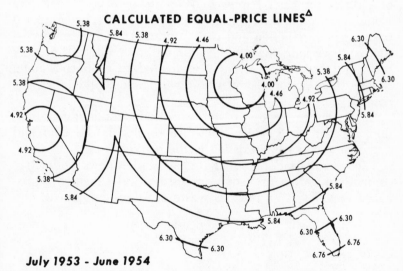

July 1953 - June 1954

†DEALERS' BUYING PRICES PER CWT, 3.5 PERCENT FOR FLUID USE.   °BASED ON PRICES IN 160 MARKETS
△BASED ON DISTANCE FROM ALTERNATIVE SUPPLY AREAS.

Figure 8.   The Price Structure for Milk. (From Agricultural Marketing Service, U. S. Department of Agriculture.)

is how close together they are. Remember that not all milk is produced in Eau Claire, Wisconsin. Remember also that local prices are affected by actions of the local inspection departments, the farmers' co-operatives, the State Milk Boards, and in many cases by Federal orders. Yet the actual prices in most parts of the country do not differ a great deal from those that would be given by the very simple formula.

Transport Costs

Our purpose here is neither to praise competition, nor to criticize it. We simply accept it as a major force in agricultural marketing.

But perhaps we should note that competitive marketing will usually—though not always—result in less transportation than will noncompetitive marketing. Sometimes competitive marketing is said to *minimize* transportation. This is true only in a limited sense. The way to minimize the transportation of milk is for each family to keep its own cow—then you would not need to transport any milk at all. If the geographical patterns of production and consumption are taken as given— that is, if we know how much milk will be produced in every town and how much is to be delivered to each consuming center—then perfect competition will, indeed, minimize the cost of transporting it.

But do not forget that patterns of production and consumption are not really given—they are results of the kind and degree of competition existing in the market.

The essential fact here is that good market news, and active competition, often prevent unnecessary and expensive cross-hauling—which is an obvious waste of labor, equipment, and money.

COSTS AND LOCATION

The cost of transporting raw material for processing and the cost of distributing finished products for sale will influence the profit position of producers and handlers. The price which a farmer receives for his product is the price at any given market less the cost of transportation and handling. The price at this market will be determined by the demand for the product and the price of similar products in other markets.

In Figure 9 the price at the farm, X, increases through the area outlined by AB so that the prices at points within the area AB are the price at X plus the cost of movement. Similarly, if X were a center of distribution for feed, the price at farms

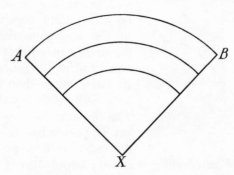

Figure 9.

located in the area outlined by the arc AB would equal the price at X plus the cost of transfer. If we could observe the price pattern surrounding a farm or any point of sale, it would resemble contours on an altitude map as in Figure 8. Each contour would represent a price, and the farther away from the point of sale, the higher the price.

In Figure 10 a market is located at M and the contours outline the prices to be paid farmers for produce sold on that market.

The price received by a farmer located at T or at other farms located on that particular distance contour would be the market price at M less nine cents per unit. A farmer located at L or on the same contour would receive the market price at M less three cents per unit. Producers located close to the market would receive a higher return than producers farther away from the market for the same product. The line SC in Figure 10 depicts the transfer costs from 0 at M up to 9 at point T, which increase at a decreasing rate. The same reason-

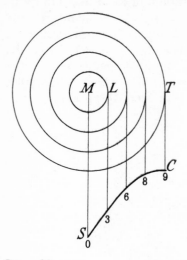

Figure 10.

ing would apply for a distributor located at M. The delivered price of his product would increase from M to T as the cost of movement increased.

If one market is closer to a seller than another market and the same transportation rates and prices are in effect, then he will receive more if he ships to the nearer market. If the difference in market prices is equal to the difference in transportation costs, then both markets will give equal returns. The decision as to which market is preferable is based on non-price considerations.

The effect of price differences on supply areas is shown in Figure 11. The price at market A is $1.00 per unit; the

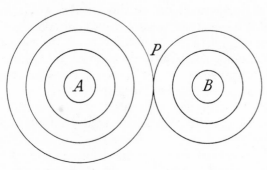

Figure 11.

price at market B is $0.98 per unit. The transportation contours are at two-cent intervals. Producers at point P would receive $0.92 in either market even though they are located closer to market B than to market A. The higher price in Market A enables it to reach out farther for supplies than market B.

Under actual market conditions, market areas are not so clearly defined. Nearby buyers may pay the same price as more distant buyers or nearby sellers may receive the same price as more distant sellers. The retail distribution of milk, of numerous beverages, of clothing, and of oil are a few examples where transportation charges are not accurately related to the relative locations of buyer and seller.

RELATIVE COSTS

The most economic location of a plant must be considered in relation to the cost of shipping raw material and the cost of shipping the finished products and by-products. The rate structure of transportation agencies has an important influence on the location of industry. This is one reason why governments maintain a control over rates and practices of carriers. If it is cheaper to ship the raw material than the finished product, then costs can be reduced by processors locating closer to the final market. If it is cheaper to handle and ship the finished product, then processing is more economically performed at the point of production. Examples can be chosen from any agricultural product for illustration and discussion.

The problem of location exists at the international level and at the local level. A retailer's choice of location for a store may be the deciding factor in his success or failure. Where are the buyers, what are their spatial buying practices? Do they prefer shopping at neighboring towns or is their preference for convenience at a nearby store? What competing markets are located in the area? A processing plant must be located where it has access to supplies and to markets. A producer must be located where he can sell his produce at a price to provide returns above costs. The cost of land or rent reflects the demand for any particular location. The rents for farm land favorably located near markets will be higher than rents of land less favorably located. Locations vary in rents according to the demand for their use. Any particular use must be profitable enough to pay such rent as would be paid in any alternative use. A store rent or a farm rent may become too high in relation to the revenue from its existing use because of the demand for housing. A processing plant located near consumers may find demand for its location for alternative uses increases the rent and the total costs of its operation to the point where it must be located in a lower rent area.

"Dumping," or Geographical Price Discrimination

The words dumping and price discrimination seem to have a bad connotation. Probably the average person thinks these things are immoral or unjust. We remind the reader again that this is not a book on morals or justice. Rather, it attempts to explain what actually goes on in the economic world around us, and especially to analyze what policies or decisions are likely to be most profitable.

In economic language, dumping simply means charging different net prices (that is, price minus freight and other handling costs) at different locations. In a similar way, discriminative buying means paying different prices (including freight and other costs) for goods bought in different locations.

There are many examples of such geographical price discrimination, both in the domestic market and especially in foreign trade. One common example is export dumping. Most countries that produce agricultural surpluses follow this practice under various names and disguises. Of course, they don't call it dumping or discrimination. But for our purposes, it is geographical price discrimination (or dumping) when the foreign purchaser can buy American wheat at less than the American price plus freight and handling costs. In this sense at least, international trade in farm products is shot full of price discriminations and dumping arrangements.

But the phenomenon is not limited to international trade by any means. There are various forms of price discrimination within the United States and in most other countries. It includes discrimination in buying as well as in selling.

In the case of buying, the geographical pattern of prices to producers is obviously affected in many cases by such things as import duties affecting international trade and various kinds of trade barriers affecting domestic markets. For example, the various schemes for "protecting" local milk markets by excluding outside milk has as its purpose and result the payment of higher prices to producers near the consuming market and lower prices to distant producers than they would otherwise obtain.

Freight rates in many cases discriminate between different

areas and different distances of shipment. For example, if
there were no discrimination in freight rates the rate from
California to New York City should be just enough higher
than the rate from California to Chicago to pay the additional
cost. Actually, many agricultural rates are the same from
California to New York City as from California to Chicago.
Somewhat similar to this example are many schemes whereby
manufacturers "absorb the freight," meaning that they charge
the same delivered prices throughout the country. Similarly,
the United States Government charges four cents to deliver
a letter whether it goes to someone in your home town or to
someone clear across the country. These are examples of uniform delivered prices, but they are discriminatory in the sense
that they do not reflect the true differences in costs.

AN EXAMPLE OF DISCRIMINATORY BUYING

A cannery has contracts to buy 4,000 tons of tomatoes at
$24 a ton delivered to the factory. It wants to increase pur-
chases next year from 4,000 tons to 5,000 tons.

Assume that the cannery is purchasing from two areas and
paying the same delivered price in each area. It is getting 2,500
tons from Area A and 1,500 from Area B. The canner knows
he must offer more than $24 a ton to get more tomatoes, but
he doesn't necessarily have to offer a higher price to every
tomato grower.

Suppose that the producers in Area A are not much interested in expanding their tomato business. Perhaps all of their
land is already in profitable uses, or perhaps the growers
prefer to spend part of their time in a local factory. But suppose farmers in Area B are anxious to expand their tomato
business. Perhaps they have lost their market for tobacco or
some other crop. Perhaps they have plenty of unused land
and labor, but they need a little incentive to make a change.

Table 5 may represent the canner's judgment concerning
the amount of contracts he could sign up in each area at
various delivered prices.

The canner might consider at least two different possible
answers. First, he might pay $27 a ton in each area. His
tomatoes would then cost him $135,000. But he could get his

Table 5

Assumed Contracts

Delivered price	Area A	Area B
$24	2,500	1,500
25	2,620	1,800
26	2,700	2,000
27	2,750	2,250
28	2,780	2,500

5,000 tons of tomatoes at lower cost by various price arrangements that discriminated between the two areas. One such arrangement would be to continue the $24 price in Area A and to raise the price in Area B to $28. Under this arrangement the tomatoes would cost him $130,000. He realizes a saving of $5,000.

AN EXAMPLE OF DISCRIMINATORY SELLING

The demand for United States wheat within the United States is known to be extremely inelastic. When increased amounts are sold on the domestic market, the total returns are decreased. In other words, the marginal returns are negative.

Probably the demand for United States wheat in export markets is somewhat elastic. In other words, when we increase exports of United States wheat, total returns are probably increased at least somewhat, indicating that marginal returns for export wheat are positive.

This means that with any given supply of United States wheat to be consumed, an increase in exports will raise the returns both in the domestic market and in the export market.

This fact has lead to many proposals for farmer-financed export programs for wheat. Such programs are currently being called "self-help" programs. They include various kinds of domestic allotment arrangements, export debentures, and certificate plans.

While the United States is not now using any of these particular programs, the government is subsidizing the export of wheat rather heavily, both under the International Wheat Agreement and under various other arrangements. In this case, the wheat grower in the United States gets a single price for wheat of a given grade, whether it is exported or not. But the foreign buyer can buy it cheaper than the buyer for the domestic market. The taxpayer makes up the difference.

This is not discriminatory pricing to the United States wheat grower, but it is discriminatory pricing to the consumers of wheat.

AN EXAMPLE OF "FREIGHT ABSORPTION"

In a purely competitive market, the shipper would never absorb any part of the freight. Rather, he would charge every buyer the same price f.o.b. shipping point. And the delivered price in any market would be the f.o.b. price plus freight.

But when competition is imperfect, the shipper will often find it profitable to absorb a part of the freight. To illustrate this fact, consider the following simple example:

Demand in markets I an J are identical:

$$q_i = a - bp_i \quad \text{and} \quad q_j = a - bp_j$$

where q_i and q_j are amounts purchased when delivered prices are p_i and p_j. But the delivered price is the net price to the shipper, (say, P_i and P_j) plus freight (say f_i and f_j).

Thus, in terms of net prices to the shipper, the demands are:

$$q_i = a - b (P_i + f_i) \quad \text{and} \quad q_j = a - b (P_j + f_j).$$

Total returns are:

$$P_i q_i = a P_i - b P_i^2 - b f_i P_i \quad \text{and} \quad P_j q_j = a P_j - b P_j^2 - b f_j P_j.$$

Marginal returns (with respect to net prices) are:

$$a - 2 b P_i - b f_i \quad \text{and} \quad a - 2 b P_j - b f_j.$$

To equalize marginal returns, the shipper must so adjust his f.o.b. prices that marginal returns are equal in the two markets. Thus, he must make

$$a - 2 b P_i - b f_i = a - 2 b P_j - b f_j$$

This requires that

$$2 b (P_i - P_j) = b (f_j - f_i)$$

or

$$P_i - P_j = \frac{f_j - f_i}{2}$$

The shipper will find it most profitable to absorb one-half the freight. Suppose, for example, that I is the local market, where $f_i = 0$. The local price, P_i will be the same as the f.o.b. price to the distant market, J, plus half the freight rate, f_j. And the delivered price in market J will be the local price plus one-half the freight rate, f_j.

A FINAL COMMENT CONCERNING GEOGRAPHICAL PRICE DISCRIMINATION

No kind of price discrimination will work for very long unless the different parts of the market can be kept separate.

To make geographical price discrimination work, the price differentials between different areas must not be so large that it is profitable to defeat the scheme by reshipping commodities from one area to another. If the United States sells wheat to Europe at a price far below that in the domestic market, some steps have to be taken to prevent this wheat from being sent back to the United States and resold at the higher price. In a somewhat similar way, the canner who paid $24 in one area and $28 in another might run into trouble. Farmers in Area A might also demand $28. They might even sell their tomatoes to farmers in Area B for, say, $26 so that each could make a profit on the deal. To prevent this, the price differentials must either be kept less than the cost of reshipment or else the whole deal must be kept secret. The canner could tell farmers in Area B that he will pay them $28 a ton, but he could warn them not to let anybody know about it.

QUESTIONS FOR DISCUSSION

1. Say you have 1,000 bushels of potatoes to sell. Assuming that your program will not affect market prices, what information would you need to find your most profitable market? Would it ever pay you more to sell in two markets than to sell your entire supply in the better single market?

2. What is dumping? Give an example of dumping:
    (a) in international trade
    (b) in domestic trade?

3. When, if ever, would it pay the shipper to "absorb" part, or all, of the freight?

SUPPLEMENTARY READING

1. Bredo, William, and Anthony S. Rojko, "Prices and Milksheds of Northeastern Markets," *Northeast Regional Publication* No. 9, University of Massachusetts Agricultural Experiment Station, Bulletin No. 47, 1952.
2. Shepherd, Geoffrey S., *Marketing Farm Products.* Ames: Iowa State College Press, 3rd ed., 1955, Ch. 14.
3. Vaile, R. S., Grether, E. T., and Cox, R., *Marketing in the American Economy.* New York: Ronald Press Company, 1952, Part V.
4. Waite, Warren C., and Harry C. Trelogan, *Agricultural Market Prices.* New York: John Wiley & Sons, Inc., 2nd ed., 1951, Ch. 7, pp. 157-182.
5. Waugh, Frederick V., *Readings on Agricultural Marketing.* Ames: Iowa State College Press, 1954, pp. 114-142. See, in particular, excerpts from von Thünin, Hoover, and Black.

12

When to Buy and Sell

An apple grower in West Virginia has 2,500 bushels of Yorks in storage. He has an offer of $1.75 a bushel in December. Should he sell now, hold until late winter, or sell part of the 2,500 bushels now, and part later?

The hog market has been dropping. Suppose you were an economist for Swift and Company. You know the company will need to buy substantial numbers of hogs within the next month or two. How would you analyze the question—should the company buy now, or wait?

Would an "ever-normal granary" program be profitable to wheat growers if they paid all the costs?

When to buy and when to sell are problems that come up every day. Decisions must be made by farmers, by processors, by speculators, by distributors. Even the final consumer makes some decisions about the timing of purchases, especially in the case of semi-durables, such as clothing.

Demand Relatively Stable

Demand for the majority of foods and fibers does not change in the same pattern that supplies of these products change. Large supplies, without a similar increase in demand, tend to force prices down. Therefore, when corn is harvested and sold by a large number of farmers, the market is glutted and prices tend to fall. From this point on, prices gain until the next seasonal production peak. In the spring and fall, the supply of pork increases and prices fall. The supply of beef generally increases at the end of summer grazing and prices

140

are lower at this time. Each product has a marketing peak coincident with lowest prices.

Marketing Firms, and Demand

Seasonal changes in supply are reflected in the practices of firms that handle agricultural products. Additional labor is required when supplies are heavy. Equipment may be specialized, so that facilities for handling supplies during the peak seasons may stand idle during the rest of the year. This makes for high unit costs.

Uncertainties

Open-market prices reflect the behavior of all farmers supplying that market. Any individual may take advantage of an expected seasonal price drop by withholding his product from the market until prices strengthen. He may plan his breeding program to take advantage of sales in the normally short-supply seasons. Weather, feeding response, and disease are examples of uncertainties, however, which are difficult to overcome by planning. They add to the fluctuations in supply characteristic of agriculture, and result in equivalent fluctuations in price. Similarly, changes occur in the prices of things which farmers must buy, such as fertilizer, wages for labor, and machinery. Unexpected changes in costs and prices create uncertainty, which must be balanced in the farm operation by diversification or other means.

Timing Under Perfect Competition

Perfect competition cannot exist unless every buyer and seller has perfect information about current supply and demand conditions, and also about the probable conditions in the future.

In such a situation, each competing buyer would try to purchase his supplies when his net costs (price plus storage) are lowest. And each seller would try to market his goods when he could expect to get the highest net price (market price minus storage). Assuming that demand is perfectly stable, the process of competition would equalize net prices over time. For example, the May price of wheat would equal the September price, plus carrying costs from September to May.

Of course, perfect competition is an abstract concept. In the actual world, price changes over time may differ rather markedly from those that would be anticipated if competition were universal and perfect and if market demand were perfectly stable. This does not necessarily mean that prices are set by some wicked, monopolistic conspiracy. Probably the most important reason for price irregularities is the fact that market information is never perfect, never complete, never exactly accurate. Moreover, some buyers and sellers have more accurate information than others do.

Another important reason why market prices sometimes seem to move contrarily is that demand is not always stable. A case in point is what Keynes [1] called the "backwardation" of the futures market. Working [2] called the same phenomenon an "inverse carrying charge." These terms describe a tendency for spot prices of grain in the fall to be higher than the price of futures for spring delivery. Keynes explained this phenomenon by saying that the spot price must exceed the forward price by the amount which the producer is ready to sacrifice in order to "hedge" himself. Working presented a more elaborate theory. But he, too, explains inverse "carrying charges" as a preference to hold actual grain. If this preference is general, the demand for grain will be higher in the fall than in the spring. In such cases, there is nothing abnormal about spot prices being higher than futures prices.

REDUCE SEASONALITY OF PRODUCTION

The seasonal pattern of production that is followed because of custom or because of natural reproduction cycles can be changed by producers. The spring milk peak can be modified

---

[1] John Maynard Keynes, *Treatise on Money*. New York: Harcourt, Brace and Co., 1930.
[2] Holbrook Working, "Theory of the Inverse Carrying Charge in Futures Markets," *Journal of Farm Economics*, Vol. XXX, No. 1, February, 1948.

by controlled breeding programs so that cows freshen at intervals during the year. Similar programs can even out hogs and beef cattle. Mature animals can be held on feed for longer or shorter periods. Even crops vary, variety by variety, in their time of maturity. The reduction of seasonality is a cost that must be returned in the price received for the product.

REDUCE SEASONALITY BY STORAGE

Again at a cost, the seasonal production of supplies moving into processing can be modified if the commodity is storable. Wheat and cotton are examples of easily stored products. Supplies can be spread equitably through the year and from year to year or released according to market requirements. The storage costs will be included in the product price. They will vary with the investment in facilities and with the length of time held.

Products such as potatoes, apples, onions, and butter can be stored for limited periods of time. These periods are in general less than the period between production peaks in any one region, although new techniques are lengthening the time that such semi-perishables can be held in good condition. The cost of storage for semi-perishables may be greater than that for storables. This usually results in a larger seasonal movement of prices of semi-perishables than in prices of "hardware" items.

Processing to Store

A further alternative is to process the product during the peak season and store it in its processed form. This, of course, does not reduce the cost of processing due to seasonality. It does enable the processor to receive greater returns from the total crop by controlling sales. This will allow for a higher price to producers. Such products as milk, fruits, and vegetables are examples. Milk which is produced in abundance in the spring can be diverted to processors for cheese, butter, and condensed, evaporated, or dried milk. Fruits and vegetables can be frozen, canned, or dried for storage. Here again, there is a time limit on storage which provides a solution for seasonal variation but not for inter-year variation. There is always the risk of lower price if stocks are held from one year to the next.

Risk of Storage

To hold a product in storage necessitates a risk. The greatest of these risks is that the market price at the time of sale will be lower than at the time of purchase, or that it will be a price less than that necessary to cover all the costs incurred. This imposes a decision which is based on expectations of future prices. A farmer holding wheat in storage on the farm instead of selling at harvest time when prices tend to be low is running the risk of prices going even lower. He is also speculating that prices will be higher than their current level. The uncertainty of the future is measured in the range of possible prices and is based on past experience and an assessment of prospective demand and supply.

The kind of risks that relate to prices may be due to unexpected events or they may be tied in with variations in economic activity better known as *business cycles*. A period of declining price expectations will dissuade producers against storage. In periods of upswing in business activity, there is greater inclination to store for speculative purposes. In either case, there can be no guarantee that market prices will be the same as expected.

A hog farmer may protect himself by storing corn for future cash sale or for feeding to hogs. A beef-feeder has a similar alternative. This introduces a flexibility which reduces the risk of loss or at least diversifies the probability of loss.

Storage Necessary to Processors

In order to maintain operations, processors must have a supply of produce on hand. This need forces them either to store or to contract for future delivery. If the processor has storage facilities, uncertainty of physical supply is minimized by carrying sufficient stocks. Such behavior, however, limits the possibility of gains should prices go down. The certainty of having a supply when needed must override the possible gains from lower prices on the open market at the time when needed. Similar risks are carried by wholesalers and retailers who must serve the public and who must have a guarantee of supply.

The particular time when a processor should buy, therefore, depends on the risk attached to future supplies. If the market is well-served from stocks carried by commercially reliable firms, it may be advantageous to buy when needed and carry a minimum inventory. The cost of storage will probably be lower for a specialized storage firm than for a processor. For a scarce commodity, the purchase and storage of supplies when available will provide a guarantee which may be essential for successful operation. Particular varieties of grain for baking, apples for pies, and flax for linen are examples.

An independent retailer generally depends on wholesale houses for storage stocks but must carry adequate operating inventories. Chain stores and other retail organizations have integrated their operations with wholesale and supply companies to remove the risk of supply shortage. Decisions of when to buy are shifted back to the wholesaler level. Speculative gains and losses are eliminated or absorbed within the organization.

"Orderly Marketing"

"Orderly marketing" is a popular slogan. Almost everyone is in favor of order and against disorder. Farm organizations and co-operative associations have been organized to bring about orderly marketing. And the Congress of the United States has voted funds so that government agencies could foster orderly marketing.

What is this orderly marketing—aside from a stirring slogan that induces farmers to pay a membership fee to an organization, or that induces Congressmen to appropriate money? The main idea seems to be that of avoiding alternate periods of glut and shortage—to even out market supplies over time—to "feed the market" so as to avoid excessive fluctuations in prices.

Thus, the idea of orderly marketing is associated with stability. Stable supplies and stable prices over time seem like desirable things. But the economist must make some reservations. Complete stability may be impossible—or, at least, too expensive. Moreover, both the farmer and the consumer are concerned with the average level of prices, as well as with stability. As a field representative of the former Federal Farm Board said, when discussing the operations of the Stabilization Corporations, "Of course, when I talk about stabilizing prices, I mean stabilizing them *up*." Farmers are usually interested in stabilizing prices up—consumers, in stabilizing prices down. Who can say whether stable prices are desirable or not, without considering the level?

Some economists have concluded that stabilization operations, such as those of the Commodity Credit Corporation, cannot affect the average level of farm prices significantly—that they can partially stabilize prices, but cannot raise the average level of prices appreciably. If all farmers believed this, there would probably be much less support for government storage programs. True, these programs have always been justified as stabilization measures. They have been associated with such phrases as "ever-normal granary" and "orderly marketing." But farmers still hope that these programs will stabilize prices up. Is the farmer interested in orderly marketing as an end in itself? Would he have much enthusiasm for it if he were convinced that it could not raise his average price?

But you may say that the consumer will benefit from stability in any case. Is this true?

Take a simple case, far removed from agriculture. For many years the New York subways operated on a fare of five cents. In the 1940's, it became apparent that the fare would have to be increased. For some time, the experts thought that a fare of seven and one-half cents would do. But, instead of two tokens for 15 cents, someone suggested a fare of five cents the first week, ten cents the second week, five cents the third week, ten cents the fourth week, and so on. The average fare would be seven and one-half cents in either case. Which deal would be better for the consumer? Each individual consumer would be *at least* as well off with the unstable fare as with the stable fare. If he chose to do so, he could use the subway exactly the same number of times each week—whether the fare was stable or unstable. If he did this, his cost would be the same in either case. But he might well choose to ride the subway more often on the weeks when the fare was five cents, and less often when it was ten cents. If so, he would do it of his own free will, because he would be better off. The unstable fare would give him an advantage that he would not get with a stable fare at the same average level.[3]

These comments are not intended as an argument in favor of disorderly marketing. They are intended only to show that the problems of when to buy and sell are not simple and are not answered satisfactorily by slogans. Of course, we all want orderly marketing. But we don't necessarily want complete stability of prices, or of supplies, over time.

Profit (or Loss) from Stabilization

For sake of illustration, imagine an oversimplified case. Assume a pattern of production and prices like this:

	Production (Million bu.)	Price (Dollars per bu.)	Farm income (Million dollars)
Year 1	500	1.00	500
Year 2	400	1.40	560
Year 3	300	2.00	600
Year 4	500	1.00	500
Year 5	400	1.40	560
Year 6	300	2.00	600

And suppose this pattern repeats itself indefinitely.

Now, a big farmer-owned stabilization corporation is set up to stabilize prices. If its operations do not affect production, the corporation will have 400 million bushels to sell each year at a price of $1.40—making an average income of 560 million dollars. Without stabilization, average income would have been:

$$\tfrac{1}{3} \ (500 + 560 + 600) = 553\tfrac{1}{3} \ \text{dollars.}$$

---

[3] The principles involved here are discussed in more detail in Frederick V. Waugh, "Does the Consumer Gain from Price Instability?", *Quarterly Journal of Economics*, August, 1944. Also, L. D. Howell, "Comment," and Gertrude Lovasy, "Further Comment," *Quarterly Journal of Economics*, February, 1945.

So the gross profit from stabilization would be $560 - 553\frac{1}{3} = 6\frac{2}{3}$ million dollars a year. This might, or might not, pay the costs of storage and administration. (Of course, if the government pays the costs, the farmer gains $6\frac{2}{3}$ million dollars. This is paid by consumers. But, in addition, the taxpayers must pay the cost of the program.) This oversimplified example does not prove anything. It only illustrates a principle. Many years ago, Ezekiel [4] made some statistical estimates of the degree to which farm income could be raised by storage operations. His estimates showed modest increases in farm income in most cases.

But theoretically such gains could be very large in certain cases. And in other cases stabilization would reduce farm income. It all depends upon the shape of the returns curve (showing farmers' incomes as a function of marketings). If the returns curve is concave downward, stabilization will raise income. If the returns curve is concave upward, stabilization will reduce income. The amount of increase or decrease in income depends upon the degree of curvature of the returns function.

Equalizing Marginal Returns Over Time

Whenever competition is imperfect—so that a firm's decisions concerning the timing of its purchases or sales affects the movement of market prices over time—it will maximize profits by equalizing net marginal returns over time—not by equalizing net prices. If the demand for apples should be elastic in the fall and inelastic in the spring—in other words, if the marginal returns were positive in the fall and negative in the spring—it would be profitable to increase apple sales in the fall and to store less for sale in the spring.

Of course, this policy would be profitable only if the demand in the fall were more elastic than in the spring. And here we are concerned with elasticity—or, better, with marginal returns—in terms of net price (that is, with price minus storage and carrying charges). The apple grower might well

---

[4] Mordecai Ezekiel, "A Statistical Examination of the Problem of Handling Annual Surpluses," *Journal of Farm Economics*, Vol. XI, No. 2, April, 1929.

find that marginal net return was greater in the spring than in the fall. This would tend to be true, if actual consumer demand were the same in every month, for the same reason that marginal net returns from distant markets are often greater than from local markets. In this case, the grower, or his co-operative, would find it profitable to "absorb" part of the storage cost—just as some industries find it profitable to absorb part of the freight to distant markets. In other words, it may often pay to hold apples in storage, even though the expected spread between fall prices and spring prices is not enough to cover the full storage cost.

Irreversibility

In geographical dumping, there is always the problem of preventing the shipment of supplies from the low-priced market to the high-priced market. But prices can sometimes be depressed at one time, and raised at another time, without any serious problem of reshipment. Time only moves in one direction. Storable commodities can be withheld from the current market and sold at some future time. In this case, you need not worry about someone taking advantage of the deal by buying at a low price later and reselling now. It cannot be done.

This is the main difference between price discrimination in time and other forms of discrimination: in space, in form, and by persons. A commodity can always be reshipped from one geographical market to another. It can be resold from one person to another. And, in some cases, the form can be changed in either direction. But it can never be transferred from the present to the past—time is always a one-way street.

QUESTIONS FOR DISCUSSION

1. What risks must a seller consider when deciding whether to sell now or later?

2. Are price fluctuations of benefit to the industry or to consumers? Do you advocate measures to increase price stabilization of agricultural products?

3. What are the guideposts for deciding when to buy or sell:

(a) In case your decisions do not affect market prices?

(b) In case they do?

4. What is "orderly marketing"?

5. What facts would you need as the basis for an intelligent decision whether to sell your apples in the fall or to store them for sale in the late winter and spring?

SUPPLEMENTARY READING

1. Working, Holbrook, "Theory of the Inverse Carrying Charges in Future Markets," *Journal of Farm Economics*, Vol. XXX, February, 1948.
2. Shepherd, G. S., *Agricultural Price Policy*. Ames: Iowa State College Press, Chs. 3 and 4.

13

What Form of Product to Sell

Milk is sold in several forms: fluid milk, cream, butter, condensed milk, cheese, and so forth. Oranges are sold as fresh fruit, canned juice, frozen juice concentrate, and other products. Wheat can be made into flour or into breakfast food or used as an ingredient in poultry feed.

These are only a few illustrations of the fact that farm products are often sold in several different forms. One common decision in marketing is that of choosing what form of a product to sell, or, more accurately, how much of the available supply to sell in each form.

Conditions of Perfect Competition

If you operate in a perfectly competitive market—that is, if your decision has no effect upon market prices—your best bet is to sell your entire supply in whatever form pays you the highest net price. In determining net price, you must, of course, allow for the cost of changing form.

For example, if you could sell fresh milk for $3.50 a hundredweight, if you can sell the butter made from 100 pounds of milk at $3.95, and if it costs you less than 45 cents to change the milk into butter, then you should sell butter. With the same prices of milk and butter, you should sell milk if your cost of changing the milk to butter is more than 45 cents.

This is a simple, obvious principle. It is the same as the principle of "orderly marketing." It leads to the equalization of net prices for different forms of a commodity in a competitive market at any time and place. For if the net prices were unequal, all competitors would try to sell in the form that returned the highest net price. We would tend to have all fluid milk or all cream, all fresh oranges or all frozen juice. This would not work out.

We are assuming here that any producer can sell his products in any form he chooses. Ordinarily this is true in the marketing of farm products. In most cases, the farmer is free to sell his products in any form he chooses.

Imperfect Competition

But perfect competition is not universal, even in agricultural marketing. Not all farmers have access to a Class I market for milk. And manufacturers of food and clothing must respect patent rights and trademarks.

More important, a few firms may have control over a substantial proportion of the total supply of milk or lemons or corn to be sold at a given time and place. Their decisions as to the proportions sold in each form will affect prices. If they sell more milk in Class I and less in Class II, they will lower the price of Class I milk and probably will raise the price of Class II milk. If they "divert" some of the lemons from the fresh market to citric acid, they will strengthen the price of fresh lemons and probably will decrease the price of citric acid a little.

In all such cases, the most profitable policy is to sell in whatever form offers the highest marginal net returns. A necessary condition for a maximum income is that sales in the various forms be so adjusted that marginal net returns are equal. This should be no surprise. It is the same principle that determines the most profitable place and time to sell. The economics of place, time, and form are identical. If you understand the principle for one, you understand it for the others.

Reversibility

After the form has been changed, it is often impossible to change a commodity back to the original form. Cracked eggs and shelled walnuts are examples. The following conversation was heard in the office of a co-operative association:

Worker: A woman is out front wanting to buy a dozen cracked eggs.

Manager: Well?

Worker: We are out of cracked eggs. What shall I do?

Manager: You had better crack up a case or two.

Does this conversation strike you as odd? It is not. The regular sound eggs are sold only at wholesale. Cracked eggs are sold to consumers at the wholesale price, or perhaps at a little less. When there is a surplus of eggs, it is important to push every outlet. The alternative is to lower prices. A good outlet for cracked eggs may well stall off a general price reduction and be quite profitable to the members of the association.

A point here is that eggs, once cracked, cannot be made whole again. Otherwise, the scheme would soon break down. Nor can you change citric acid back into fresh lemons, nor breakfast cereals back into grains.

But, although these processes themselves are not reversible, the demands for the different forms are not completely independent. This is a practical matter of some importance—especially from a long-term point of view. The diversion of fresh lemons into citric acid may be quite profitable for a while,[1] even though the price of citric acid is driven so low that it returns the farmer a very low net price on the tree. His net marginal returns for citric acid may still be greater than his net marginal returns from the fresh market. This is so because the demand curve for citric acid is almost flat while the demand curve for fresh lemons falls sharply to the right.

But in the long run, large supplies and low prices of citric acid probably reduce the demand for fresh lemons. This means that at least part of the profits from diversion are lost. The lemon growers of California suspect this to be true, and are not so enthusiastic about diversion as they once were.

The theory of maximizing net income by equalizing marginal net returns is usually explained only for the case of "independent markets," where the demand in any segment of the market is unaffected by prices in other segments. The

---

[1] Professor Sidney Hoos of California has studied such diversions.

mathematical principle can be rather easily extended to the general case, but we shall not attempt to do it in this book.

But without any elaborate theory, the main point should be clear. The various forms of a commodity usually compete with one another. Where they are close substitutes for one another, even the immediate gains from discrimination will naturally be small. Where two forms are not now close substitutes, they may become close substitutes in the future if the consumer is given the chance to buy a new form of a food at a lower price.

Yet there doubtless are cases where the new form opens up a new market without reducing the old market appreciably. Many canned fruits and vegetables illustrate this. The canned product is available the year around. It does more than replace demand for fresh foods. It adds new demands.

Practical Diversion Problems

Changing the form of a farm product is one of the most popular ways of diverting surpluses from the normal channels of trade. In many cases this helps to strengthen prices in the regular market. It also is usually more profitable to change the surplus products into some other form than it is to destroy them. Thus, when potatoes are used for starch or for alcohol, they usually give the farmer at least a little income which he would not get if they were destroyed.

The practical difficulty is, of course, that each individual farmer wants to sell in the higher-priced market. He would be willing to have someone else's products diverted and sold at a low price, but he will not willingly sell his own products at less than the price in the regular market. For that reason, most such diversion operations are carried on by strong farmer co-operative associations or under marketing agreements and orders. In either case, the farmer gets a "blended price"; that is, he gets the weighted average of prices in both parts of the market.

Even when farmers are not organized, and when there is no marketing agreement, a government agency may encourage the diversion of surpluses by making payments to producers. The potato diversion programs in past years illustrate this procedure.

Industrial Uses

A popular panacea for the farm problem which crops up from time to time is the diversion of surplus farm products into new industrial uses.

If the new industrial uses are fully competitive and can afford to pay the going price for farm products, they do not represent diversion at all. In this case the new industrial uses are fully desirable and beneficial to everyone. Research that holds promise of developing such unsubsidized industrial markets has great merit.

Some of the industrial uses that are discussed from time to time probably would not be workable without either a subsidy or some sort of compulsory law. A case in point is grain alcohol. Without question, we could make alcohol from surplus corn or other grains. However, we have plenty of alcohol now. Also, if growers of corn or other grains at today's market prices made it into alcohol, they would have to raise the price of alcohol in order to make a profit. To overcome these difficulties in arithmetic they would have to do one of two things: (1) the government might subsidize grain alcohol by making payments to alcohol manufacturers, or (2) the Congress might pass a law requiring that a certain percentage of alcohol be mixed with gasoline.

Qualities and Grades

A product can be divided into types and grades so that the total income from sales will be further increased. The product is graded according to quality or according to some other characteristic preferred by buyers. To the extent that a product meets these specifications, a higher price will be paid. If the product does not meet these specifications, a lower price will be offered by the buyer or, in the extreme case, the product will be rejected.

It is to the benefit of the seller, therefore, to know what characteristics will provide him with market premiums. The stage of picking sweet corn, the type of crate for lettuce, the variety of strawberries, and the fat on hogs are examples of product characteristics or of handling methods that can influence the price to be received. A poorly packed load of fruit or overripe peaches may be discounted by the buyer and the price agreed on will be lower than would have been the case if more care had been exercised in packing or in shipping. An individual farmer may seek out premium markets that will pay him a higher price. The higher price can be obtained, however, only because of some additional time or effort in the growing or packing of a product.

The grades, established by the U.S.D.A. and by private shippers or merchants, are based on certain product characteristics which in general call for different prices. They will be discussed in Chapter 21.

QUESTIONS FOR DISCUSSION

1. Why is the form in which his product is sold important to the producer?
2. What is a diversion program? Give an example of its use to increase farm income.
3. Discuss the economics of classified milk prices.
4. Illustrate how grading a product for sale can:
   (a) Increase net income or
   (b) Decrease net income.

SUPPLEMENTARY READING

1. Black, J. D., *Introduction to Economics for Agriculture*. New York: The Macmillan Company, 1953, pp. 125-134.
2. Vaile, Grether, and Cox, *Marketing in the American Economy*. New York: Ronald Press Company, 1952, Ch. 18.

14

From Whom to Buy
and to Whom to Sell

The economist often thinks of the market as being entirely impersonal. In many cases it is. In many cases the buyer makes an open offer to buy all of a commodity that is offered by anybody at a stated price. In a similar manner, a chain store, for example, advertises broilers at 29 cents a pound and will sell to anybody who will buy at that price. However, not all offers in the actual market are open and impersonal. Some of them are very limited.

We might note in passing that there are still some outright prejudices, although they are probably gradually disappearing. Not so many years ago there was a common saying, "Nobody Irish need apply." Many business concerns would not deal with Negroes. These and similar prejudices are not based upon economics. A study of such matters belongs in sociology and psychology and will not be analyzed here.

In addition to outright prejudices, buyers and sellers are doubtless affected by all sorts of noneconomic considerations that sometimes go under the name of "favoritism." Tobacco buyers are often accused, rightly or wrongly, of favoring certain growers by giving them better than the average market price. They may do this because the grower is a relative, because he owes the buyer money, or simply because the buyer likes his looks. In a somewhat similar manner, the farmer may play favorites in picking out a local buyer or commission man to handle his hogs or his potatoes. He may make this important decision for such reasons as habit and custom, perhaps preferring to stay with the same dealer who always handled his business and the business of his father.

This chapter is not concerned with such noneconomic concepts as favoritism and prejudice. Rather, it deals with the same kind of subjects that we have been considering in Chapters 10 through 13. In many cases, it is possible for the buyer or seller to discriminate not only by place, time, or form, but also by person. He may find that an open offer to everyone at a uniform price is not his most profitable arrangement. Rather, he may find that he can make a profit by charging different prices to different consumers, or by paying different prices to different suppliers. This is the basic reason for many of the special deals and discounts that are common today, especially where such deals are limited to certain groups of consumers—perhaps to members of particular clubs or co-operative associations, or perhaps to groups of consumers with low incomes.

Equalizing Marginal Net Returns

By now you should not be surprised to find that the principle of equal marginal net returns applies to this case, too. Of course, this doesn't mean that you can always make a profit from any kind of discrimination, whether by place, time, form, or person. You could easily discriminate the wrong way around (granting the lower prices to the wrong people, for example), thus making a loss instead of a profit. If the market is divided into two parts in such a way that the demand presumably is about the same thing in each part, there is no economic justification for charging different prices. Joan Robinson [1] illustrated this well by her remark that a barber would not necessarily make a profit by charging red-haired people a lower price than he charged other people for a haircut. Such a practice would be profitable only if the demand of red-haired people as a group were more elastic than that of other people—that is, if the marginal net returns

---

[1] Joan Robinson, *Economics of Imperfect Competition.* New York: The Macmillan Company, 1938, Chs. 15 and 16.

from the red-haired customers were greater than those from other customers.

Unfortunately, the economist does not have very accurate information concerning differences between the demands of different consumer groups. However, there are at least some theoretical reasons, supported by some empirical evidence, why people with low incomes have more elastic demands for most commodities and services than do higher-income people. To the extent that this is true, any marketing plan in which prices are related to the ability of the individual consumer to pay tends to be profitable. The low-income consumer, having the advantage of a lower price, will expand his consumption of a commodity. He will bid it away from the consumer with a higher income, forcing the higher-income consumer to pay a considerably higher price.

EXAMPLES

There are many examples of this situation in modern marketing. However, most of them are somewhat covered up by at least nominal differences in qualities, packages, and so on. Perhaps the simplest cases, and those of greatest interest to agriculture, are several former and existing programs of the Department of Agriculture to make surplus foods available to some groups of domestic consumers at less than the regular market price. Technically, this might include some give-away programs, such as direct distribution of food surpluses to needy families. In this case, the needy families are charged a zero price. However, we shall consider only examples in which certain groups of consumers pay a price that is lower than that of the regular market.

The Nickel Milk Program

Perhaps the simplest illustration of such a program was the nickel milk program that was carried on in six large cities for some years before World War II. In this case, low-income families could buy milk for five cents a quart, while the regular delivered price was 14 cents. This was obviously a two-price arrangement. Only families with very low incomes were allowed to buy milk for five cents.

The costs of the nickel milk program were split four ways: (1) The participating family went to a depot, picked up the milk, and paid for it, relieving the distributor of all the costs of delivering milk and collecting debts; (2) the milk distributor handled this business at much less than the usual margin (this was partly a reflection of the lower costs and partly a willingness to bid a lower price to get additional sales); (3) the dairy farmer accepted a lower price for the milk used in this program; and (4) the Federal Government paid a small subsidy.

Several surveys conducted during the experiment indicated that participating families greatly increased their consumption of milk, thus helping to relieve a surplus situation in the market.

School Lunch Program

The school lunch program is carried on co-operatively by Federal, state, and local governments. In general, these programs provide low-priced lunches to school children.

The Federal Government from time to time provides certain surplus foods for school lunches. Also, the Federal, state, and local governments provide cash subsidies through which local authorities can buy foods needed in a school child's diet, whether or not these particular foods are in surplus.

The low-priced school lunches are available to millions of school children throughout the United States. Most children pay for their lunches, but children from low-income families can usually get their lunches free.

In addition to the program providing complete lunches, there has been in recent years a great deal of interest in the so-called "special milk program" which provides school children with extra milk at a price substantially below the regular delivered market price.

These school programs are, of course, aimed mainly at better diets and better nutrition, including the education of school children in nutrition, in the hope that they will acquire good eating habits which will stay with them in the future. In addition, however, these programs often benefit farmers, especially when they induce school children to eat more of certain foods which may be in surplus.

Former Food Stamp Plan

Beginning in 1939 the United States Department of Agriculture undertook a little experiment in Rochester, New York. In this case various categories of families on relief were allowed to buy $1.50 worth of food stamps for $1. These food stamps could be used to buy food in any ordinary retail store. The stamps were of two different colors. The orange-colored stamps could be used to buy any food the family wanted, while the blue stamps could be used only to buy foods that were on a "surplus list." Without question, the plan gave the participating families increased purchasing power for foods in general. How much of this increased purchasing power was concentrated on the particular foods on the surplus list is somewhat questionable. The surplus list was often so long as to be rather ineffective.

As in the case of school lunches, the stamp plan was designed partly for the purpose of improving diets and nutrition and partly for the purpose of raising farmers' incomes. The dual-purpose nature of the program was both a strength and a weakness. It was a strength because both farmers and consumers were interested. It was a weakness because many farmers thought the expense should not be borne by the budget of the Department of Agriculture.

Effects Upon Farm Income

The effects of such programs upon farm income are sometimes greatly underestimated. Some people assume, for example, that since the farmer gets about 45 cents of the consumer's food dollar, he gets only about $450,000 out of each million dollars spent by the government on a food program for low-income families. This would be true if the food-distribution plan increased the supply of foods so that non-participants got just as much food as before. In other words, it would be true if the increased consumption of participating families represented additional supplies that would not have been marketed except for the program.

In the usual case, at least in the short run, these programs are more nearly in the nature of a diversion of part of the supply from high-income to low-income families. Whether or not we have a food stamp plan, for example, practically all the hog supply or the milk supply gets consumed. There is seldom, if ever, a surplus of these foods, in the sense that any considerable amount cannot be sold at any price. What happens is that the price to everyone is driven down to the point where the entire supply gets taken off the market. Now, if we start something like a food stamp plan, the main effect is to let low-income families get a larger proportion of the food supply, leaving a smaller proportion for the rest of us who can afford to pay higher prices for food. This important effect has often been forgotten. It is the most important part.

For example, a food stamp plan, if it were put into effect today, would probably not be available to more than five per cent of the families in the United States. In considering the effect upon farm income, the most important question is the extent to which it would strengthen prices of the 95 per cent of the families that pay the market price. Even a stamp plan covering less than five per cent of the families would probably help to strengthen market prices slightly.

As a practical matter, the effect of stamp plans and similar programs upon farm income depends in part upon such things as adequate policing to make sure that the stamps are really used for food and that the food bought by participants is not resold to nonparticipants. These are important, practical matters. They never can be handled perfectly. But a well-policed food stamp plan (one that would keep chiseling down to a practicable minimum) might be quite profitable to agriculture as well as a benefit to low-income families. The really important question is not, "How much of the government subsidy gets back to farmers?" but, "How does the program affect total expenditures for food (by participants and nonparticipants alike), and how does it affect marketing costs?" An effective food stamp plan costing, say, one-half billion dollars, might well raise farm income by more than one-half billion dollars.

QUESTIONS FOR DISCUSSION

1. What motives would a buyer have for differentiating between sellers?

2. What is the economic basis for sellers differentiating their products between buyers?

3. List government and non-government programs that practice price differentiation. What is their effect on income distribution?

SUPPLEMENTARY READING

1. Black, John D., *Dairy Industry and the A.A.A.* Washington, D.C.: Brookings Institution, 1935.
2. Robinson, Joan, *Economics of Imperfect Competition.* New York: The Macmillan Company, 1938, Ch. 15.
3. Shepherd, G. S., *Marketing Farm Products.* Ames: Iowa State College Press, 3rd ed., 1955, Ch. 10.

15

Risk in Marketing

What Risks to Accept

Agricultural marketing is a risky business. You may make a killing. But you may lose your shirt. Further on we shall discuss some of the ways of reducing risks or of avoiding them. But the only sure way of avoiding the risks of agricultural marketing is to go into some other business. If you want to make money from agricultural marketing, you will have to accept many risks. You must be prepared to lose sometimes.

How, then, can you determine what risks to take? You want a policy that is *likely* to give you a good profit and very *unlikely* to ruin you financially.

This problem is very similar to that of gambling at games of chance. Gamblers have always been concerned with the probabilities of winning at dice, roulette, blackjack, and similar games. Such modern mathematicians as Uspensky [1] and Feller [2] have added to our knowledge about the subject called "The Ruin of Gamblers" or "The Duration of Play." This concerns the probability that a gambler will be ruined (that is, that his capital will be lost), and the probability that he will still have some money left after 10, 100, 1,000, or any other number of games. The marketer might profit from an understanding of these matters.

First, the marketer should have a clear understanding of

---

[1] J. V. Uspensky, *Introduction to Mathematical Probability*. New York: McGraw-Hill Book Company, Inc., 1937.
[2] W. Feller, *An Introduction to Probability Theory and Its Applications*. New York: John Wiley & Sons, Inc., Vol. I, 1950.

his *expectation*. Take, first, a simple case where there are only two possibilities: Suppose that the chance that your shipment will be wrecked is $\frac{1}{1000}$, and that in this case you would lose $2,000. The chance that it will *not* be wrecked is $\frac{999}{1000}$. Suppose that in this case you win $10. Your expectation—that is, your expected gain is:

$$\$(-2000 \cdot \frac{1}{1000} + 10 \cdot \frac{999}{1000}) = \$7.99.$$

In case there were several possibilities, each involving different gains or losses, you would simply multiply each (positive or negative) gain by its probability and take the sum of the possible gain and loss as your expected gain.

The first lesson here is to avoid those risks where your expectation is negative. This includes all games in gambling houses. For example, as roulette is played in Las Vegas, your expectation is —$1/19; that is, if you make a long series of bets, you should expect to lose about $1 of each $19. If you played 1,900 games at even or odd, or at red or black, you would win about 900 games, and lose about 1,000 games. Since the bank offers even money, your loss would be about $100 in 1,900 bets of $1 each. The longer you play, the more certain you are to lose.

Your problem is to assess the probabilities and the gains and losses to be made in each case. To do this for a marketing situation is by no means as easy a job as it is to figure a simple game like roulette. But it must be done if you are to decide intelligently which risks to take.

Second, you may want to avoid many risks, even though your expected gain is positive. Take the simple example above, where your expected gain is $7.99. This is the *average* gain you would make if you took the risk many times. But you might suffer one or more losses of $2,000 each. If you can't afford to lose $2,000 occasionally, you had better avoid this risk, perhaps by insuring against it, if the insurance rate is less than $9.99. Say that you can insure against the risk for $6. Then you reduce your expected gain to:

$$\$(0 \cdot \frac{1}{1000} + 10 \cdot \frac{999}{1000} - 6) = \$3.99,$$

but you have completely avoided the probability of loss from wreckage.

Third, even if your expected gain is positive, you may be ruined unless you have adequate capital. A gambling house is often a very profitable affair for two reasons: (1) it plays only those games where the *house* has a positive expectation, and (2) it has enough capital so that the likelihood of "breaking the bank" is very remote. To be sure, it takes risks. But this kind of risk-taking is quite profitable.

Expected and Unpredictable Risks

We may classify risks or hazards into those that can be expected on the basis of past experience and those that are fortuitous and not predictable.

In the first type of risk, rain or drought may ruin a crop or reduce the pasture. Disease may hit the livestock or crop and reduce production unexpectedly. A product may be spoiled in transit, or fire may take a warehouse.

Many of these events can be insured against by the pooling of risks with other members of an industry through an insurance company or by co-operation. The risk then becomes measurable as a cost and assumes dollar proportions. The real cost of damage is not always measurable in dollar terms, for example, where good will or trade relations are concerned. However, the history of similar events facilitates calculation of the probability that it will occur again and calculation of the cost in terms of insurance premiums or necessary savings.

Risks of the second type are somewhat more difficult to measure. War, politics, and technological change are examples. Actions by legislators on tariffs, government support prices for agricultural products, interstate barriers to trade or defense spending can place unexpected burdens on particular firms or industries. Similarly, legislative action can open markets for which an industry is not well prepared and which may have lasting effects on the competitive position of its members.

There may be population shifts because of war or unexpected economic developments which reduce the market in a particular location. A plant or a store built on the expectation of certain sales or purchases may be faced with a declining population or a decline in the number of producers from which supplies can be purchased economically.

Technological change which outdates existing facilities, methods, or products seldom can be foreseen. Maintaining a supply of liquid capital for new equipment or for change-over in response to new findings or techniques is a cost. Similarly, new products and new competitors provide a risk of sales loss that must be met and that becomes an operating cast.

Reducing Physical Risks

The physical loss of a product from spoilage can be reduced by improved storage or improved transportation methods and facilities, and also by prestorage treatment or conditioning. Refrigerated cars and icing facilities, or methods of packing and handling, are areas where improvements would reduce loss. There is a considerable financial loss each year from the bruising and mishandling of livestock in transit. Potato bruising and exposure to sunlight are other examples of loss in transit. Improved methods developed by research can reduce this type of risk even if they cannot eliminate it. The adoption of new techniques, however, must provide expected dollar savings greater than any additional cost involved before it can be justified.

Physical loss in storage is a risk that varies with the perishability of the product. Research in methods of reducing spoilage is finding methods of lengthening the market period for potatoes, apples, and other semi-perishables by means of temperature and humidity control as well as by chemical preservatives. Loss from insects, common for grains and cotton in storage, and moisture control present hazards that are being met by new methods.

Risks of Price Change

One of the greatest risks in agricultural production and marketing is the risk of price change between the time when plans are made or produce purchased and the time of final sale. The unexpected change in price because of unexpected changes in supply or demand is one of agriculture's oldest problems and one which is the basis for many marketing institutions.

The uncertainty of future prices applies to any particular year or season as well as to secular or long-run price changes. Plans for breeding, planting, or future sales based on expected prices can become uneconomic because of price changes. A price change between the purchase and sale of a product may result in an unexpected loss or gain. Here the history of price changes is of limited value in prediction. There are seasonal price changes for agricultural products which are predictable and which are expected. There are certain demand cycles which are predictable and expected. The risk involved is that the expected will not happen and financial loss will result. There is no way of predicting technological developments and their adoption by competing firms.

PRICE FLUCTUATIONS AND MARKET INSTITUTIONS

Rapid changes in prices from day to day on through the growing period are costly. They are more costly if they are unexpected, representing, as they do, the difference between planned income and actual income for one party to a contract. The producer may base his production plans on certain prevailing or expected price relationships. Unexpected price declines at the time of sale will provide an income to the seller less than expected and windfall gains to the buyer. A dealer buying at a certain price may have to resell at a much lower price because of price changes. A processor may contract to buy certain products in the future at prices based on prevailing market prices of produce. Unexpected upward changes in price may remove the profitability of the project.

There are numerous market tactics that aim to compensate for the cost of probable price fluctuations during the marketing process. (1) Dealers may use a percentage markup so that buying and selling prices move together and the risk of price change is shifted back to producers or forward to consumers. (2) Contract prices may be sufficiently high or low to compensate for the probability of unforeseen price movements. (3) Prices may be administered by the government or the industry and based on an economic index within allowable limits of fluctuation. The price-support programs for agricultural commodities provide security of sale at certain minimum price levels. Fluctuations above this level, however, still maintain the disadvantages of rapid change. (4) There may be agreement between members of an industry either to limit their price competition or to establish limits to daily price changes.

REDUCING PRICE RISK

The more information on supplies and prospective demand that is available to buyers and sellers, the more accurate basis they have to predict prices and the less likely it is that sudden price changes will occur. Since we can never have perfect knowledge of future market demand and supplies, however, there will be market uncertainty from unanticipated price changes. Modern transportation and news facilities have reduced those uncertainties greatly, and the institutions developed under more speculative times also provide services for reducing market risk.

Trading in Futures

Facilities for price stabilization and risk minimization are more available to growers and handlers of storable products than to handlers of perishables. The ability to store enables sellers to spread sales through the year. The holding of commodities for later sale requires financial resources to meet costs of storage and there is an opportunity cost of holding the product rather than money. Storing to control sales is, therefore, a form of speculation or gamble against price changes, and as such is to be regarded as a cost. The producer, the dealer, or the processor must bear this cost if supplies are to move regularly to market to meet consumer requirements. Efforts to get rid of or to minimize this cost as well as to supply credit to the store mark the development of certain institutional devices.

One of these devices is the futures market, which enables the owner of the product to enter a contract for future delivery for a specific month and for an agreed price. The future price at which he can contract to sell will reflect the prevailing estimate of demand and supply expected at the future date.

Commodity Exchange

Trading in contracts to buy and in contracts to sell is done through the commodity exchanges, or contract markets organized for this purpose.

The contract markets operating in the United States cover such commodities as wheat, corn, oats, rye, soybeans, grain sorghums, butter, eggs, potatoes, cotton, wool tops, cottonseed oil, soybean oil, lard, cottonseed meal, soybean meal, beans, and shorts.

Membership in these exchanges is limited to established traders with adequate financial support and credit. All suppliers wishing to deal in futures must operate through these approved agents dealing in a regulated contract market. Such markets are under Federal regulation by the Grain Futures Act of 1922. This law was strengthened and amended to include other commodities and renamed the Commodity Exchange Act. The Act prohibits certain practices that overstep the original purpose of the exchange, such as price manipulation, cornering of the market, cheating or defrauding customers, making false reports, or disseminating false crop and market information.

The Commodity Exchange Act further states that exchanges or contract markets must:

(1) be located at a terminal market with sufficient cash sales to reflect current market prices and be under official inspection approved by the Secretary of Agriculture.

(2) provide for the keeping of records and filing of reports for audit by the Federal Government.

(3) provide for the prevention of price manipulation and other prohibited practices.

(4) admit co-operatives to membership on equal terms with others.

All persons handling or executing orders on the exchange must register with the Secretary of Agriculture and provide adequate protection for customer funds.

To prevent undue influence on market prices, there are legal limits on the amount of speculative purchases or sales by a person in a single day and on the speculative holdings of futures contracts. At the request of the Secretary of Agriculture, the exchanges must limit their daily price fluctuations in any commodity.

Commodities in which there is futures trading but which are not covered by the Commodity Exchange Act are wool, hides, rubber, cocoa beans, coffee, sugar, apples, onions, pepper, dressed turkeys, and frozen eggs.

There are two main types of trading in the commodity exchanges: (1) hedging and (2) speculation.

HEDGING

The value of the commodity exchanges to merchants or handlers of agricultural products and to processors of raw materials is in the hedging operation. The success of this operation depends on the spread between cash and future prices. When this spread is constantly changing, the hedging operation becomes more difficult and inexperienced hedgers may lose more than they gain. The relationship between cash and futures, however, tends to equal the accepted cost of storage between the two periods, and as cash prices change, forward prices change also. There is no guarantee that this will happen, however.

As an example, a crusher buys 20,000 bushels of soybeans for storage and sale during the marketing year. When the time of sale arrives, for some unexpected reason, the market price may have dropped considerably below his purchase price. At the time of purchase, however, he asks his agent on the commodity exchange to sell a futures contract to deliver the same quantity of soybeans at the prevailing futures price, provided this price is sufficiently above the cash price to compensate for storage costs. At the time he sells his holdings of soybeans, he can make up any loss from reduced price by the sale of his futures contract and the purchase of a new one at a lower price. This assumes an ideal situation in which the changes in spot prices and in future prices are exactly equal. Often there would be more or less difference, so hedging would not be perfect.

HEDGING TRANSACTIONS

Cash Transactions	*Future Transactions*
Nov. 1 Buys 20,000 at $2.50	Nov. 1 Sells 20,000 May futures at $2.90
Jan. 1 Sells 20,000 at 2.30	Jan. 1 Buys 20,000 May futures at 2.70
Loss per bushel .... .20	Gain per bushel .... .20

This type of transaction is a stabilizing influence on the market, but it is made possible chiefly by shifting the risk cost to the second type of trading, namely, speculation.

SPECULATION

The major part of the trading in the commodity exchanges is speculative. The purchase and sale of futures contracts are based on estimates of probable price changes during the trading year. To buy a futures contract and then sell at a price difference above the margin for storage costs will provide a gain to the speculator. Therefore, in periods of rising or inflationary price movements, trading in futures is likely to be more active than in periods of stable or declining prices. The speculators who deal through brokers often have no connection or apparent knowledge of the commodities in which they trade. Small businessmen, clerks, teachers, and retired persons are examples, although producers sometimes try their hand at speculation. The buying and selling of futures, however, may serve the purpose of moderating price fluctuations and prevents futures prices from getting too far out of line with cash prices. The hedging operation is provided with a market for the purchase and sale of futures contracts to protect the cash contracts from losses due to price changes. Speculation in grain futures, like that on the stock exchange, directs the gambling urge into economically useful channels.

The success of speculation depends on the accuracy with which speculators guess about the future scarcity of a commodity. If they guess a future short supply, they will tend to buy more for future delivery. This has the effect of reducing available supplies and raising current prices. However, the future supplies are increased and prices are less high than they would have been without the speculative purchases. To the extent that speculators guess correctly, they perform the social service of evening out supplies and prices through the year. However, bad guesses tend to aggravate supply and price variations, to the detriment of efficient distribution.

The futures market reflected the outbreak of war in Korea. In the month after hostilities began, lard futures prices increased 41 per cent, cottonseed 32 per cent, and soybeans 26 per cent—all commodities which futures traders guessed would be in greater demand. Prices of egg and corn futures, in comparison, increased only 5 per cent.

Opportunity for Speculation

In the security markets, the Federal Reserve Board establishes the amount of margin or down payment required by speculators. In the case of commodities, however, the margin requirements are established by the individual exchanges. Those vary between commodities and from time to time and apply to "outside" traders rather than to members of the exchange who execute their own transactions.

MARGIN REQUIREMENTS FOR VARIOUS EXCHANGES, JULY 28, 1950

Commodity	Market	Contract	Price	Margin	Margin as % of price
Wheat	Chicago	5,000 bu.	$11,356	$1,250	11.0
Corn	Chicago	5,000 bu.	7,618	600	7.9
Soybeans	Chicago	5,000 bu.	13,200	1,500	11.4
Lard	Chicago	40,000 lb.	6,220	800	12.9
Cotton	New Orleans	100 bales	19,325	3,000	15.5
Sugar	New York	112,000 lb.	6,339	400	6.3
Onions	Chicago	600 bags	1,038	300	28.9

Credit and Risk

Credit is an essential and established feature in the marketing and distribution of agricultural products. Credit is a process of lending and borrowing. Goods are forwarded to a borrower and payment is made at some later date. The amount of credit allowed and the length of time the lender can allow for repayment depend on the financial resources of the lender and his need for money. A farmer selling to a processor generally needs cash to pay for his factors of production. The amount of credit he can allow the buyer or the time before he is paid is generally limited. The milk check, the egg check, or the wheat check is not far behind the delivery date of the produce. A processor or wholesaler selling to a retailer, on the other hand, is frequently called upon to supply goods on credit. Payment is made after the goods have been resold to consumers.

The length of time between planting and harvesting is sufficiently long to create financial needs by producers. Depending on their expected market, some credit on the prospective crop may be provided by the processor or the handler. The risk of a crop loss is carried by the lender, but the cost of this risk is charged to the borrower as interest to be collected when the crop is sold. A beef feeder may obtain a loan on feeders, to be repaid when the beef is finally sold. The credit is an essential part of the operation. The lender runs the risk of loss, and the cost of this loan to the borrower will reflect the risks involved.

Sale of produce when the buyer and seller are at distant points is facilitated by the use of credit. The futures market is based on credit. A futures contract can be held by means of a nominal down payment and the rest as credit. The sale of non-food items, such as household equipment and automobiles, is frequently made on credit with repayment extending over several months. The interest is payment for the credit extended to the consumer. Retail credit for food products is less extensive and limited to milk or credit at the local store or by the butcher on a weekly or monthly basis. Extended retail credit for food is not considered good business by retailers as compared with credit for durable goods which can be repossessed if necessary.

The risk of providing credit by banks to wholesalers, by dealers to producers, or by wholesalers to retailers is borne by the marketing system. This risk is in the nature of a cost which will be added to the final price of each product. Deductions from prices received by producers or handlers by the party providing credit is profitable to them only if expectations are fulfilled. Where the risk of loss is greater, the cost of credit will be higher. Consumers, producers, and handlers will have certain credit ratings by the trade and by bankers. Certain standards of risk are established to guide their credit allowances and to minimize risk to them. The wheels of the marketing industries run more smoothly and goods move faster from producer to consumer because of credit.

Avoiding Risk

Risk may not be eliminated, but perhaps it can be shifted. A farmer who sells all his produce at harvest time is shifting the risk of future price changes to the buyer. A handler who buys and sells futures is shifting the risk to the speculator. A processor who buys only for current operations and holds no stocks is shifting the risk of physical loss to the holder of storage stocks. Processors who enter into contracts with producers for the delivery of specific quantities of crops are reducing the risk of supply shortages.

A milk dealer may operate under legislation providing minimum prices to be paid producers and to be charged to consumers. The announced prices and the fixed margin reduce his risk, and those costs normally associated with price risk can be eliminated. Similarly, a retailer may operate on a percentage markup basis. If supplies are provided from an independent wholesaler, then much of the risk has been shifted. Consumers carry the risk of income change and wholesalers carry the risk of spoilage or of supply shortage. Hand-to-mouth buying may successfully shift certain risks to specialized agencies better equipped to insure such risks or to carry the risk at the lowest possible cost.

Size of Operation and Risk

Spreading of certain risks is more possible for a large firm than for a one-plant firm. For example, a firm may have several retail outlets in numerous locations. The risk of loss due to poor location is thus less critical. Unsold stock can be transferred to other stores or the unprofitable store can be closed down. Similarly, in an integrated processing firm, if one plant faces supply difficulties due to its location, it can be supplied from other plants.

Processors or retail stores can be assured the provision of adequate supplies when needed by vertical integration. This is exemplified when chain stores own the assembly, processing, and storage facilities under one management. Risk from unexpected supply shortage or competitive bidding during times of increased demand is reduced.

The control over supplies to influence price may be attempted by producer associations, or by agreement among large firms handling the greater part of a particular product. The integration under one management of all the functions between production and consumption increases the size of the operation. The total investment is increased, the management problems are increased, and the possible loss from poor decisions is increased. On the other hand, control over supplies reduces both physical and price risk. A large poultry processor can contract for supplies of poultry with individual growers. The risk of price change is absorbed by the processor, and, given a sufficiently large operation, this risk is reduced for the individual producers. The supply risk has been reduced and perhaps, if the share of the market is large, the risk of price change has been reduced. There are in general more choices of markets available to a large firm with facilities for diversification and storage.

Research in utilization, in processing, and in markets is more feasible for a large firm with the resources needed for such activities. Market risks can be reduced if more knowledge and information is accumulated and made available to those making decisions. In larger firms, research is possible on quality controls, on storage, and on the physical properties of their commodities, with the objective of reducing loss and costs. Such information is not usually available to small firms except as supplied by trade associations and by government and state college research organizations.

QUESTIONS FOR DISCUSSION

1. List the risks of a farmer and those of a processor of agricultural products.

2. What has private industry done to reduce intra-year price fluctuations of agricultural products? What have government programs done?

3. How does hedging reduce risk?

4. What are the costs of risks to a processor?

5. What do you think about "forward pricing" of farm products, that is, price floors announced by the government before planting time?

6. "Nothing ventured, nothing gained." If you are going to make a good income in marketing, you will have to take chances. But you want to find deals where the *expected income* more than covers the *expected costs*. What does this mean, and how can you study your *expectations?*

SUPPLEMENTARY READING

1. Duddy, E. A., and D. H. Revzen, *Marketing*. New York: McGraw-Hill Book Company, Inc., 1947, Ch. V.

2. Schultz, T. W., *Production and Welfare of Agriculture*. New York: The Macmillan Company, 1949, especially pp. 95-99.

3. Shepherd, G. S., *Marketing Farm Products*. Ames: Iowa State College Press, 1946, Chs. 9 and 10.

PART 3

MARKETING POLICIES
OF ORGANIZED GROUPS

16

Group Action and Economic Power

Organized groups of various kinds do a large part of modern agricultural marketing. These organized groups include farmers' co-operative associations. They include a great variety of trade associations. Also, in a sense they include hundreds of corporations engaged in processing and distributing farm products.

Purposes of Group Action

People organize themselves in groups for all sorts of reasons. Some farmers may join a co-operative association partly, at least, for social reasons. They may like the members of the co-operative, enjoy going to occasional meetings, and like to serve on committees. In this book, of course, we are concerned mainly with economics. No doubt the main reason prompting most people or firms to join an organization is the hope of getting some economic benefits.

One of the common benefits is that of reduced costs. A large plant can often process milk or fruit at a much lower cost than could several small plants. By organizing a co-operative association, a large group of farmers may be able to build and maintain a large, efficient plant. Similar savings are often made by merging several small firms into a large one.

Many trade associations were organized partly for the purpose of obtaining more accurate, comprehensive, and up-to-date market information for their members. For example, the National Canners Association and the National Cotton Council obtain detailed statistics on such things as storage holdings and current consumption rates in various parts of the country and even throughout the world. Such trade associations usually make full use of available government statistics, such as crop reports and market news information. But they usually add detailed information of interest to their members.

Many trade associations are also interested in the establishment of "codes of business ethics," including such things as the adoption of uniform standards of quality.

Practically all organized groups try in one way or another to promote the sale of their products. Some of them carry on large programs of market research, development, and advertising. Among many examples that could be given are the promotional programs that have been carried on for many years by organized groups of orange growers, both in California and Florida, and the promotional programs of the American Dairy Association.

Economic Power

A further reason for organizing, in most cases, is to get some degree of economic power. An individual or small firm carries practically no weight in the market. A large, organized group, on the other hand, can often exert a considerable amount of power. A corporation or a labor union, for example, does not necessarily have to accept whatever prices are offered. It has the power to withhold its products until it is ready to make a deal. Moreover, an organized group often has the power to affect state and Federal legislation.

Most organized groups talk very little about this aim of economic power. They might even deny any such aim. This is because they want to avoid controversies about the enforcement of "antitrust" laws. At present, our state and Federal policies in this area are not at all clear. Some economists seek a tightening of the antitrust program to prevent further mergers and to foster small independent business. Other economists believe that the organization of still larger groups is necessary to bring about maximum economy. Some, like Galbraith,[1] argue that the public is protected by countervailing power—

---

[1] John Kenneth Galbraith, *American Capitalism*. Boston: Houghton Mifflin Co., 1952.

that is, that the power of one organized group is offset by the power of another organized group.

These issues are far from settled. Some of the agricultural economists who have done good work in this area are Nicholls [2] and Hoffman.[3]

Oligopoly and Oligopsony

It is easy to understand the theory of monopoly. But it is very doubtful if there is any such thing as monopoly anywhere in the agricultural marketing system. Rather, there are many situations dominated by a few large concerns. If this group of large concerns is engaged in selling a product, it is an *oligopoly*. If it is engaged in buying a product, it is an *oligopsony*. The theories of oligopoly and oligopsony are difficult and rather vague. The plain fact is that no one can be sure how a group of large buyers or a group of large sellers will act. There may be a good deal of collusion (or co-operation) between the members of the group. On the other hand, there may even be cutthroat competition, which can be much more deadly than the simple, old-fashioned competition between individuals.

In some cases, there is a tendency for one member of the group to become the dominant leader. The leader usually decides what the price is going to be and the others follow suit. Many people think, for example, that a few big packers, big tobacco companies, and big milk distributors exert a great influence over prices, and that the rest of the industry tends to follow suit.

In a somewhat similar way, many observers have thought they saw evidence of "market sharing" on the part of big buyers of farm products. This is a situation where each of the large buyers keeps a fairly constant percentage of the total market but does not try very hard to expand his share at the expense of one of his competitors.

---

[2] Wm. H. Nicholls, *Imperfect Competition Within Agricultural Industries.* Ames: Iowa State College Press, 1941.
[3] A. C. Hoffman, "Large-Scale Organization in the Food Industries." Washington, D.C.: Temporary National Economic Committee, Monograph No. 35, 1940.

In any case, the theories of oligopoly and oligopsony that are applicable to agricultural marketing are necessarily somewhat different from those applying to other industries. The big buyer or seller of farm products usually has no control over production. The meat packer handles all the hogs that are offered to him. The miller buys and handles all the wheat that is offered. These men do not adjust their prices so that the marginal revenue from the crop equals the marginal cost of producing the crop. Rather, they adjust their handling margins to maximize their net income. Their net income is gross margin times quantity minus expenses. If they put the price too high to the consumer or too low to the farmer, they will lose business. Thus, even in cases where competition is not severe, a large processor or distributor has to be careful not to set his handling margin too high.

Integration to Increase Economic Power

The economic reason for integration is the joining together or consolidation of the decision-making function. Where before integration several managers made independent decisions on pricing and production for their firms, after integration a single decision is made by the integrator. This ability to make decisions is exchanged for increased security of income. For example, independent pea growers have made their own decisions on the acreage to be planted, the variety to be grown, and the market in which to sell. A canner agrees to buy the peas each year at a prearranged price, provided that he can control the acreage, variety, and time of harvest. The individual growers who accept the terms of the contract are integrated into the pea-canning industry.[1] The canner has

---

[1] Many economists do not consider such contractual arrangements as constituting genuine "integration," preferring to restrict the term to instances of ownership of the integrated units. The authors recognize that there is justification for this preference, but have chosen to follow the usage of most agricultural economists in classifying such "contract farming" as a form of integration. Cf. R. Trifon, "Guides for Speculation About the Vertical Integration of Agriculture with Allied Industries," *Journal of Farm Economics*, Vol. XLI, No. 4, p. 734, Nov. 1959.

increased his security of supply and can more safely plan his canning operation and market development. The grower is assured of a market and has greater security of income. The economic power of both is increased. Similar examples can be drawn from the poultry industry. The owner of a poultry-dressing plant contracts for the production and delivery of broilers. In place of buying his supplies of birds on the open market, he contracts with the growers. In return for their labor and the use of their capital equipment and buildings, he provides feed, veterinary care, chicks, managerial advice, and a fixed return per bird. In this way much of the risk to the grower is eliminated. His operation becomes integrated with the operation of the dressing plant. The processor has obtained control over an assured supply.[2] In turn, the dressing plant may contract for delivery to a retailer under certain specifications. In return he will receive guarantees of price and quantity of sales. The growers, the dressing-plant owner, and the retail outlet are now integrated, and this association has increased the efficiency in production and in marketing and the economic power of the industry.

A retail chain store can guarantee its supplies by owning wholesaler operations, processing plants, and transportation facilities and by contracting with growers. This is *vertical integration*. The consolidation of the decision-making function at the same level of production is *horizontal integration*. For example, a number of food retailers will consolidate their ownership and buying operations into one operation.

A group of dairy farmers may decide to gain the advantages of large-scale feeding and milking and integrate their operations under one management in return for a guaranteed market for their milk and reduced labor responsibility.

The consolidation of independent operations gains two objectives. It provides an industry with reduced costs from economies of scale because of the more complete utilization of equipment and capital. In addition, the economic power of

---

[2] In the United States, the integrator is often a feedsman who seeks guaranteed outlets for his mixed feeds. Processors are more often the "integrators" in Canada, however.

the industry in the market is increased. While this will probably not be complete monopoly power, it may improve the industry's ability to influence prices and profit margins.

QUESTIONS FOR DISCUSSION

1. What gains are there for producers or dealers of agricultural products from group action?

2. Discuss the meaning of *monopoly, oligopoly,* and *oligopsony.* Give examples in agriculture.

3. Is integration in agriculture conducive to imperfect competition?

SUPPLEMENTARY READING

1. Nicholls, Wm. H., "Imperfect Competition in Agricultural Processing and Distributing Industries," *Canadian Journal of Economics and Political Science,* Vol. X, No. 2, May, 1944.
2. Seaver, S. K., "An Appraisal of Vertical Integration in the Broiler Industry," *Journal of Farm Economics,* Vol. XXXIX, December, 1957, p. 1487.

17

Policies of Farmers' Organizations

The organization of farmers into groups historically has received greatest impetus during times of economic troubles such as falling farm prices, increasing costs of transportation and farm machinery, and inadequate markets. While gatherings or groups for social activities and fairs have been a factor in local organizations, it has taken some general problem affecting the pocketbooks of farmers to provide a basis for state and national group action.

Following the initial encouragement to railroad expansion by local and state governments, the Federal Government policy of land grants to railroads provided a point for disagreement and criticism by farmers. This was particularly true when the rail rates on farm products were raised and the price of farm products fell. Cries of monopoly and exploitation were heard in the land, and in the 1870's there were attempts to organize unions of farmers in several states. Conventions of farmers called for equal justice to all, opposed the granting of public lands to railroads, and proposed the organization of collective buying groups for farm equipment and supplies.

The Grange started in the 1870's as a fraternal organization but soon became the central agency for voicing farmers' discontent. Local Grange membership provided representatives from 32 states at an annual session in St. Louis in 1874. The purposes of the Grange were to fight those business interests believed to be exploiting farmers and to substitute direct buying for buying through middlemen. The membership became concerned also with the unfavorable competitive position under which farmers sold their produce.

The low prices and money shortage of 1874 encouraged the formation of the Greenback political party supported by farmers. The Farmers' Alliance started in the 1880's from local farmer associations, under various names such as the Brothers of Freedom, the Arkansas Agricultural Wheel, and the Northern Farmers' Alliance. The general complaints and rallying points were low prices, monopoly by railroads in the establishment of rail rates or tariffs, and banking policies. These farm organizations were instrumental, for example, in obtaining passage of the Interstate Commerce Act (1887) for regulating the railroads.

The Farmers' Union, which was started by a newspaperman in Texas and which was built up at a financial loss to himself, became a national union in 1907. Prior to this time, state unions had attempted to influence the price received for cotton in the South. Their method was to withhold cotton from the market by building warehouses for storage. The Farmers' Union Cotton Company of Memphis had offices in England in order to sell directly from warehouses to English mills. From then on, there were attempts to operate businesses for the buying of farm supplies at lower prices. Several successful supply co-operatives were established, as well as livestock and grain commissions.

The newly established orange industry in California, faced with falling prices, looked with suspicion on the spreads retained by middlemen. They organized a co-operative for the marketing of their fruit. Opposition by buyers and inadequate co-operation among growers resulted in the failure of the earliest attempt. Continued attempts at co-operation by fruit growers resulted in the eventual formation in 1905 of the California Fruit Growers Exchange, which has operated successfully since then (now Sunkist Growers, Inc.). Continued discontent with prices and their inferior bargaining position convinced Pacific Coast farmers of the need for farmer co-operatives.

The co-operative movement was given impetus following World War I, when farm prices fell disastrously. Aaron Sapiro attempted to organize producers of basic crops into co-operatives for the control of supply to influence price. While not all farmer co-operatives had the same success in controlling the markets that the Pacific Coast Fruit Growers had, steps were made to improve the economic power of agricultural producers.

The Farm Bureau Federation, developed as a mouthpiece for farmers in Federal and state legislatures, and the farm bloc in Congress came to life as a politically potent force. Farmers' interests shifted to questions of markets for farm products. The Federal Government was forced to adopt measures to find new markets or to improve domestic market prices. Questions of supply control and price stability became national farm issues. The Secretary of Agriculture urged the land grant colleges to offer more economics and marketing in their curriculums. A Department of Markets was established in the United States Department of Agriculture and the economic issues of farm income and markets became of more importance than the problems of increased production.

Farmers' Marketing Co-operatives

When we speak of farmers' marketing organizations, we think particularly of co-operatives. But in historical perspective, the co-operative marketing association as we know it today is a relatively recent and highly specialized organization. Farmers' first organized response to marketing problems took the form chiefly of political action groups. Many of them came also, however, to sponsor economic action in the form of collective buying of supplies or selling of products, being forerunners of the modern co-operatives.

A marketing co-operative is a firm owned by the producers whose product it sells. Members of the co-operative are generally limited to one share and one vote on policy. This limitation differentiates the ownership pattern of a co-operative from a corporation. In a corporation, ownership may be concentrated in the hands of one or a few, thus ensuring control over major policies. The equal distribution of voting power among marketing co-operative membership prevents such concentration of control. Profits of a corporation are distributed according to the number of shares held. In a co-operative, the net returns are distributed among members according to their sales. Market costs are not eliminated, and in some cases they may even be higher than for privately owned marketing firms. The satisfaction of knowing that unexpected market gains will be returned to producers as patronage dividends and that members will receive equal consideration when markets outlets are reduced are among the justifications for membership.

A privately owned and operated marketing firm exists for the purpose of making money for its owners. They hope to make a return on their invested capital that is at least as high as they could get by investing in some other kind of business. A co-operative, likewise, exists for the purpose of making money for its owners, the grower-members. But it does this not by paying them a return on their capital investment. Instead, it seeks to get them better prices, taking into account patronage dividends, than they could get by trading with private firms.

SHOULD A FARMER JOIN A CO-OPERATIVE?

The individual farmer faces the decision whether to join or not to join a co-operative. The farmers who establish and operate a co-operative have decisions to make regarding the kinds of activities it will engage in and how it will conduct them.

A chief incentive to the individual farmer for joining a marketing co-operative is the anticipation that it will get him better returns for his product. The farmer is most likely to be concerned about this in times when markets are poor and prices are low—and especially if marketing firms appear at the same time to be prosperous, suggesting that there are profits in marketing that he could share by joining a farmer-owned marketing enterprise. Hence, co-operatives are likely to grow most vigorously in times of agricultural depression.

The farsighted farmer, however, will look beyond the prospect of immediate returns. Co-operatives—especially those that own and operate extensive facilities—require capital investment. They cannot economically be set up and dismantled over short periods. A farmer should consider, therefore, whether the market situation is such that there is continuing prospect of benefits from operating a co-operative. He should recognize that the success of the co-operative depends upon support by himself and the other members. In joining, he is making a long-term commitment.

He should also recognize that, even though at any particular time the co-operative provides no better returns than he could get by selling individually, the very existence of the co-operative may still be of benefit. This is because a well-managed co-operative may force competing private marketing firms to operate more efficiently, give better service, and pay higher prices.

A co-operative may increase the economic security of the member farmer himself and his neighbors. It can offer an assured outlet so that, when demand is poor, he will not find himself simply cut off from his accustomed market. The impact of a decreased demand will be shared equitably between himself and the other members. The very fact of joining with other farmers in an organization for their common benefit may itself be attractive.

Against these considerations of possible benefit are the costs of membership—both costs in money, since capital investment is usually necessary, and costs in time and energy, since the dispersed membership control of a co-operative makes it necessary that members keep an intelligent watch over its activities, serve on committees, and otherwise work actively in its behalf in order for it to continue to serve them effectively. In addition, there is the giving up of independence of individual action in marketing—the opportunity to drive a better bargain through trading on one's own.

HOW SHOULD A CO-OPERATIVE OPERATE?

The scope of activities carried on by farmers' marketing co-operatives varies widely. One broad classification is between bargaining co-operatives and operating co-operatives. The bargaining co-operatives act chiefly as agents for their members collectively in selling products. They seek, through the volume of supplies that they control, to obtain better prices than the members could obtain individually. But they do little or no actual physical handling of the products.

Operating co-operatives, on the other hand, actually operate facilities for such things as assembling, grading, packing, selling, processing, shipping, and distributing. They seek to make money for their members not just through greater bargaining strength in selling, but through providing better and more efficient marketing services than their members could obtain otherwise. Local operating co-operatives often join together in regional organizations—co-operatives of co-operatives—that carry on quite large-scale operations, even to the point of national-brand promotion, as in the case of *Sunkist* citrus fruits.

Whether a co-operative should limit its activities to bargaining or should go into actual marketing operations depends chiefly on the market situation in the commodity with which it is dealing. Ownership and operation of facilities take substantial capital. Such operations are attractive chiefly in situations in which the services rendered by private marketing firms are inadequate, or are inefficiently conducted, so that there is a prospect that the co-operative could do the job better and more cheaply.

Actual practice varies from commodity to commodity. A substantial proportion of manufactured dairy products, for example, is processed in plants of operating co-operatives. While operating co-operatives are important in some fluid milk markets, the larger volume of milk sold co-operatively for fluid use is through bargaining associations that do little or no actual handling. Co-operatives are important in the shipping of livestock, but very few carry on actual meat-packing operations. The bulk of sugar-beet production is sold through bargaining co-operatives. A substantial volume of many fresh fruits and vegetables is shipped from co-operatively operated assembly plants. In processed fruits and vegetables, both bargaining and operating co-operatives are involved. The scope of operations of operating co-operatives varies widely, but the greatest concentration is at the farm end of the marketing process. Historically, the trend has been for bargaining co-operatives to take on at least limited operating functions.

GOVERNMENT ENCOURAGES CO-OPERATIVES

The Federal Government, through the Sherman Act of 1890, the Clayton Act of 1914, and the Robinson-Patman Act of 1936, placed restrictions on the collective action of firms in the purchase and sale of goods in trade to preserve the "free and natural flow of trade in the channels of interstate commerce."

On the other hand, by the Capper-Volstead Act of 1922, producers were encouraged to act together "in collecting, processing, preparing for market, handling and marketing in interstate commerce." In 1926 a division of Co-operative Marketing was established in the United States Department of Agriculture to promote knowledge of the co-operative principles and to provide producers with pertinent marketing information and research in all phases of co-operation. These functions are now the responsibilities of the Farmer Cooperative Service. Here was legislative recognition that the agricultural marketing co-operatives could provide some relief from the uncertainties of farm income.

The benefits of co-operation are not limited to marketing. There are co-operatives for the purchase of producer supplies, co-operatives for consumers, co-operative breeding associations, and co-operative schools. The nature of the activity may differ but the principles remain the same.

INTEGRATION OF CO-OPERATIVES

Common problems in marketing have encouraged the integration of local co-operatives into regional and national affiliations. Such co-operatives as the California Fruit Growers Exchange and the Sun Maid Raisin Growers Association were formed from local associations federating with common objectives. Regional co-operatives, such as Land O'Lakes Creameries and the Dairymen's League, were formed by the integration of state and local co-operatives. That is, local co-operatives have joined hands across state boundaries to increase the size of business and to reduce costs of operation. The Co-operative Grange League Federation of New York and the Eastern States Farmers' Exchange are examples of this expansion. In addition, many nationally affiliated co-operatives are diversifying the products handled in order to strengthen their profit position.

Many local associations are further affiliated with national organizations such as the National Livestock Producers Association, the National Co-operative Milk Producers Federation, and the National Wool Marketing Corporation. Some surrender of individual sovereignty may be necessary to standardize certain marketing procedures or to adopt certain cost-saving measures. This type of affiliation is a combination of horizontal and vertical integration. It makes possible the sharing of information and the mutual evaluation of problems so that regional and national considerations assist in what might otherwise be a series of contradictory or unrelated local decisions.[1]

SIMILAR PROBLEMS BUT DIFFERENT WAYS OF DECISION-MAKING

The ownership pattern of marketing co-operatives does not reduce the operational problems of processing and distributing produce. Markets still remain essentially competitive and the produce handled by co-operatives must compete with produce handled by privately owned firms. They must compete for consumer preferences, maintain quality, and sell at prices that will provide growers with adequate returns.

Management decisions are frequently more difficult if the growers are fully represented on the board of directors, as is the case with most marketing co-operatives. This problem will vary among co-operatives according to the degree of authority given to the management of a firm or federation. Management of a co-operative selling agency or a co-operative packing plant faces different kinds of decisions from those that are faced by a producer acting as a single individual. Unless this is fully appreciated by growers, the efficiency of operation can be reduced considerably. A large private corporation with a diversity of

---

[1] See J. A. Knapp, *Journal of Farm Economics*, Vol. XXXII, No. 4, November, 1950.

interests and functions may similarly experience diseconomies of scale because of the method by which management decisions are made. There is a greater likelihood, however, that a privately owned enterprise will have a more flexible management than a growers' co-operative and will be better able to capitalize on unexpected market changes.

The operating co-operative that owns mills, packing houses, or canneries must attain the same efficiency as privately owned operations if it is to be justified in the returns to members. When net returns to members are less than those to be obtained by selling to private market firms, the basic structure of the co-operative is weakened.

Bargaining co-operatives, on the other hand, operate few facilities. Their justification is at the bargaining table, where they agree on price with buyers and handlers of their produce. The aim of this type of co-operative is, by representing a significant proportion of the producers or of total production, to equalize the bargaining power between buyers and sellers in agreement on price and conditions of sale.

Non-Farm Co-operatives

In answer to the chain stores' economies of scale, independent grocers have formed co-operatives to obtain cost reductions that enable them to compete. Such co-operative chains are sometimes organized and operated on the initiative of the retailers themselves, who set up their own wholesaling services, sometimes—in the so-called "voluntary chains"—with the sponsorship of an independent wholesaler who finds his own existence threatened by growth of chain distributors. The services co-operatively provided range from mere joint procurement all the way to provision of extensive management supervision and the advertising of co-operatively promoted brands.

Organization for Political Pressure

The Granger movement was initially an association of farmers whose purpose was the exchange of information between members and the encouragement of social activities for otherwise isolated farm families. It was not long, however, before the association became involved in problems of farm markets and prices. In so doing, they exerted influence on legislators, particularly in their demands for reducing railroad company privileges. As demands grew for federal action to help farmers maintain income, numerous farm organizations were formed specifically to influence congressmen in supporting legislation such as the McNary-Haugen Bill. The American Farm Bureau Federation and the Farmers' Union have both been politically active in the support of farm legislation.

Registered lobbyists in Washington, D. C., numbering among the thousands, represent associations and trade organizations and attempt to influence legislation favorable to the interests they represent. The passage of legislation by Congress and by state legislatures is a reflection of the majority opinion of members of those bodies. Members' opinions are formulated from opinions and interests expressed by the legislators' constituents. If the voice is powerful enough, then the Congressman must respond by voting in favor of the home interests, otherwise he will be out of a job. The more vocal interests are the ones most likely to be heard frequently.

QUESTIONS FOR DISCUSSION

1. What are the reasons for farmers' co-operative marketing associations?
2. How can co-operatives improve the efficiency of food distribution?

SUPPLEMENTARY READING

1. Bakken and Schaars, *Economics of Co-operative Marketing.* New York: McGraw-Hill Book Company, Inc., 1937, Chs. 5, 6, 7, 16, and 17.
2. Koller, E. F., "Co-operatives in a Capitalist Economy," *Journal of Farm Economics,* Vol. XXIX, No. 4, Part 2, November, 1947, pp. 1133-1144.
3. Stern, K., "Co-operatives in a Changing Agriculture," *Journal of Farm Economics,* Vol. XXXIX, No. 5, December, 1957, pp. 1271-1298.

18

Policies of Trade Associations

The Organization of Trade Associations

The assembly, processing, and distribution of agricultural products are accomplished by wholesalers, retailers, brokers, plant operators, and truckers. These firms may be independently owned or they may form part of large corporate organizations. The exchange of ideas by discussion of mutual problems is accomplished by means of trade associations. A milk dealers' association, a retailers' association, and a truckers' association are examples. The associations are organized around particular commodities or around particular functions. Members frequently are competitors on the same markets, that is, they are rivals for the same customers.

Trade ethics, distribution of useful information, co-ordination of activities in case of a national emergency, the use of common facilities, and measures to influence legislators are all topics for agreement by association members. The organization is kept active by means of contributions or fees from members, and a full-time secretary with office or staff is the focal point for activities. Periodic trade news and information pertinent to their common activities are distributed to members, while an elected executive committee establishes policy. Local associations frequently have regional or national affiliations, and, as stated previously, there are numerous associations with representatives in the national as well as state capitals to act as watchdogs or to pursue specific policies significant to the association that hires them.

The Independent Grocers' Alliance is an example of voluntary integration to gain the benefits from economies of scale in wholesaling and the gains from large-lot purchases. By association, the independents also hope to gain the price advantages obtained by the chain stores. The livestock marketing associations are concerned with developing a market for members. These associations provide a functional service by actively participating in some trade activity.

Commodity Exchanges

Similarly, firms buying and selling regularly soon appreciated the need for a clearinghouse to ensure knowledge of prices and location of potential buyers or sellers. The commodity exchanges were organized to facilitate trading in many commodities. The New York Produce Exchange was organized in 1850, the Chicago Board of Trade in 1848, and the New Orleans Cotton Exchange in 1871.

The purposes of the exchanges are to:

(1) Provide a central trading place.
(2) Agree on ethics of competition and trade.
(3) Agree on certain standard measures of grades and inspections.
(4) Exchange market information.

A central building and a trading floor are provided for members, and a call board records daily transactions and prices. The success of this type of organization depends on the proportion of total sales in the market which are transacted and recorded through the exchange. Membership in the exchange is limited to established traders with adequate financial resources and credit. Besides cash sales, futures trading is conducted in wheat, corn, oats, rye, soybeans, butter, eggs, potatoes, cotton, cottonseed and soybean oil and meal, grain sorghums, lard, beans, and shorts. Commodity exchanges have attained so important a position in marketing that Federal legislation has been enacted to regulate their operation. The Commodity Exchange Act prohibits price manipulation, cheating or defrauding customers, making false reports, and disseminating false crop and market information. (See page 170.)

Joint Producer-Trade Organizations

Appreciation that market expansion is beneficial to both producers and distributors may encourage them to co-operate in a joint association. The most common association of this type is concerned with advertising and market promotions. The American Dairy Association, for example, operates on contributions from milk producers and milk dealers. The common aim is to increase milk sales or discourage a decline in milk consumption. The Cotton Council is a similar type of association. The voluntary co-operation of independent producers and distributors is somewhat unique. The job of selling has previously been carried almost entirely by the firms processing and handling the product. As the current trend toward greater organization among producer groups continues, similar joint efforts are to be expected. This will also be true if vertical integration of producers and handlers continues at its present rate.

There are examples of poultry producers' associations being formed to exchange information on producer problems that have later developed into joint industry associations concerned primarily with sales promotion and legislation affecting the industry.

Consumer Organizations

There have been some attempts to develop consumer co-operatives, often sponsored by labor craft unions. By means of these consumer associations, leaders of craft unions planned to gain price advantages from quantity purchases of food for their members. This practice has never become very widespread in the United States.

The modern labor movement helped to organize the Council for Co-operative Development in 1947. There were ten international unions and four co-operative organizations in the Council. Both A.F.L. and C.I.O. unions attempted organization of consumer co-operatives, but no widespread interest by labor union members has developed.

Organization of consumers has never been very successful in the United States. Consumer co-operatives aimed at returning to consumers any profit from distribution and selling have been more common in Europe. Occasional attempts have been made to organize housewives in revolt against prices of certain basic foods, but these have been temporary phenomena.

The formation of associations for the marketing of food or services is a competitive means to reduce costs. Imperfect competition that extracts monopolistic profits or the inefficient operation of marketing facilities by private owners that raises costs is sufficient reason for consumers to organize. Bargaining by consumers for lower prices can be effective only when alternative supplies are available. The organization of an association to actively participate in marketing with the purpose of passing on to consumers savings in the form of lower prices or dividends has proved a useful competitive device. Consumers' co-operatives have made their greatest progress in fields where inefficiency has been present. The threat of a potential consumer co-operative may diminish the potential for monopolies or inefficient operations.

Buyer co-operation has been successful in rural electrification, in food retailing to a lesser extent, and in housing, insurance, and credit services. It speaks well for food retailers that the opportunity for consumers to co-operate in establishing rival firms exists, yet at the same time such co-operatives account for only a small proportion of the industry.

Functions Performed by Associations

INFORMATION, EDUCATION, AND RESEARCH

The voluntary association of producers or distribution firms for the exchange of trade information is frequently the original reason for organizations of this type. A trade journal published by the association has educational value. Annual meetings provide a sounding board for new ideas and for solutions of problems common to members of the industry. The intellectual stimulus provided by speakers and writers from other fields encourages new ideas and increased efficiency. There may be occasions when the financial resources of an association will allow for a research unit. This unit will conduct research on problems specifically affecting the industries which the association represents.

MANAGERIAL SERVICES

The pooling of resources may allow an association to hire the full- or part-time services of specialists and consultants not otherwise available to individual members. For example, a lawyer may be hired in cases of court action or as an advisor on the legal implications of trade policy. Another form of hired service is the establishment of uniform cost accounting methods or the study of the unit costs of production or distribution. The association may organize management training schools for its members to keep up with the research findings of other firms and of colleges and universities.

ADVERTISING AND PROMOTION

The cost of general advertising can be paid for by an association at a lower unit cost per member than if each member hired an individual firm to do the work. Brand advertising would still be the job of each firm with different brands, but agreement on advertising policy and the pooling of ideas for a common aim may attain the objectives more economically.

OPERATION OF MARKETS

Many co-operative marketing associations own their marketing facilities. A livestock marketing association may own the stockyard and auction pens, thus minimizing commission payments. Ownership of a farmers' exchange or wholesale market facilities by an association of traders will increase their individual returns by returning profits to members.

JOINT BUYING, SELLING, AND HANDLING

The purpose of the co-operative associations is to reduce costs or to share gains by joint action. That is to say, prices may be reduced from quantity discounts. Selling costs may be reduced by common ownership of facilities by competitive firms. An association may obtain lower shipping costs by combining l.c.l. shipments on long hauls.

Organizations Versus Specialized Firms

The provision of services by trade organizations is generally the outgrowth of need. An organization may be established to provide a needed service. Or an existing organization may undertake new services as members become aware of new needs and possibilities. Many services provided by associations could be furnished by private specialized firms. The livestock yards, the grain elevators, the cotton gins, the research, and the publicity are all services that can be provided by private firms. Therefore, the relative advantages of the two types of ownership should be compared. The original conditions under which the association first purchased and operated facilities may have changed. Whereas before there were no alternatives, there may now be numerous choices. Whereas the association originally provided the only steady outlet, now there may be many. Continuation of the service can be justified if costs are as low as in competing privately owned alternatives. If they are higher, then members will be paying more than necessary for the services provided or will be getting less than the normal return on capital invested in the jointly owned facilities. If, however, the benefits to members are greater because of the association, its operation can be justified.

Bargaining Associations

Bargaining associations are organized specifically for improving the income position of a group of producers, just as a labor union is intended to improve the wages and real income of its members. A few buyers with many sellers provides unequal bargaining strength. The bargaining association is intended to rectify this. The association representative bargains with the buyer. The effectiveness of such pressure for higher prices or improved market conditions depends upon the availability of alternatives to the buyer. Hence, there are advantages of widespread membership in a co-operative, so that the bulk of the supply of the commodity within the market area can be controlled.

Protecting Vested Interests

An association of merchants may promote measures for stabilizing prices and for reducing price competition. This would be particularly true among small businesses faced with potential competition from operations large enough to reduce costs.

Such measures may require the support of legislation at the state or Federal level. The enactment of "Fair Trade" laws in many states is an example. They permit contracts that establish minimum retail prices for products. The price includes a marketing spread large enough to provide adequate returns to small merchants.

Codes of business behavior among handlers and distributors are established by associations. Such codes may include agreements not to raid another's trading territory with price concessions. They may include standard costing practices, so that certain agreed profit rates or spreads will be used in product pricing.

In cases where individual firms violate the association's agreed trading practices—as in the case of discount houses or peddlers who do not have the cost of a regular place of business—an established association may adopt counter measures to drive them out of the market. Such measures may include organized pressure on the manufacturers or producers of the products being sold and on the suppliers of the factors of production necessary to the operations. By the use of ethical codes, sometimes justified and sometimes not, tradesmen can retain their share of the business.

If prices are retained at levels sufficient to provide returns on investment higher than in other enterprises, then the pressure for entry by competing firms selling at lower prices will be greater than if returns are nominal. Similarly, if prices are at levels that provide a relatively low return on capital, the pressure from "price cutters" will be reduced.

Some industry groups have promoted "buy-at-home" campaigns and perhaps have supported tariffs or other measures to reduce competition. The pricing and marketing methods followed are associated with the respectability and stability necessary for a continued supply of reliable products.

Organizations of retail firms are subject to conflict on price and selling policies. The chain stores and supermarkets compete with one another but also have sufficient buying power to exert an influence on prices to be paid growers and handlers. Attempts to reduce the economic impact of chain stores on the independent grocers during the 1930's resulted in various types of tax legislation and other forms of restrictions. Similarly, legislation was attempted by an automobile dealers' association to protect car dealers from the manufacturers' economic power. Druggists organized to maintain margins for drugstore operators against cut-rate competition.

Supply Controls

During periods of unstable or falling farm prices, the idea of controlling supply becomes popular. By this technique, supplies are so fed to the market that prices are stabilized. Produce is withheld when the market is weak and sold when the market improves. Of course, this idea does not work out well in practice unless some group of farmers or dealers has tight control over most of the supplies in some area.

Associations can establish grades and introduce quality controls through centralized grading and "trademarks." These will facilitate product differentiation for the purpose of raising prices. A seal of approval by an established association may introduce considerable inelasticity into demand. The relationship of an association trademark with quality and reliability is an accomplishment of considerable value to producers and a means of raising prices.

Conflict of Interests

The increase in economic power created by the formation of associations of producers, processors, or handlers of agricultural products is likely to create conflicts not present in atomistic competition. The attainment and preservation of a preferred position or advantage in the market require continuous activity. This activity may take the form of observing the behavior of competitors in order to be ready with counter measures of advertising, promotion, or price concessions. It may take the form of exerting influence on legislators dealing with questions of price and trade regulations to ensure favorable treatment. It may also take the form of restricting the entry into a particular line of production or market by new competitors. The election of salaried officers may in itself create a vested interest in which the officials seek to enlarge and perpetuate their influence by exaggerating conflicts of interest that will justify their claims of service to their members.

The influence of associations will vary with their size and with the scope of their activities and their effectiveness in controlling or affecting members' policies and actions. Limitations to the scope of action are, of course, imposed by government laws and regulations, as by the antitrust laws or by regulation of the activities of paid lobbyists.

The grades and standards established by the government frequently conflict with the grade policy of an association or group. Where the grading is voluntary, this presents no particular problem, but attempts to enforce grades or grade specifications create conflict with the association's grade policy. Equally possible, of course, is that the association, because it represents a large segment of an industry, can facilitate, amplify, and assist in government grade and standards policies.

A cotton growers' association, for example, can influence legislation on export policies or on programs for industrial development in other countries as a means of protecting their potential markets. A lamb growers' association can exert pressure on the administration to suspend the grades. A milk dealers' association may provide considerable resources to protect legislation favorable to its member firms irrespective of the total industry welfare. A farmers' bargaining association may not agree with price and procurement policies of processors and a deadlock may ensue, resolved only by increased consumer prices.

Similar examples could be given of interest conflicts which find expression through associations and organizations of food producers and handlers. As price competition has become less important and non-price competition more important, such types of pressure and counter pressure as we have outlined take on added significance in a competitive economy of interest groups. It is a policy of government, as the next part will discuss, to act as mediator between various groups for the benefit of all.

QUESTIONS FOR DISCUSSION

1. What are the advantages of belonging to a trade association?
2. Why are there so few consumer co-operatives in the United States?
3. Are there possible dangers in the growth of strong trade associations?

SUPPLEMENTARY READING

1. Galbraith, J. K., *American Capitalism*. Boston: Houghton Mifflin Company, 1952.
2. Palamountain, J. C., Jr., *The Politics of Distribution*. Cambridge, Mass.: Harvard University Press, 1955.
3. Rhodes, V. J., "How the Marking of Beef Grades Was Obtained," *Journal of Farm Economics*, Vol. XLII, No. 1, Feb. 1960.

PART 4

MARKETING POLICIES OF GOVERNMENT

19

Government in Marketing

Governments are taking an increasingly active hand in agricultural marketing. This is true of local, state, and Federal governments. It is true not only in the United States, but also in most other countries throughout the world. Before World War I, governmental programs in this field were small, inexpensive, and quite limited in scope. Since that time, they have grown in size, expense, and scope. The growth has not been steady: rather, it has been in a series of spurts. The biggest spurts came during the two World Wars and the Great Depression of the 1930's. Some of these programs (wartime food rationing and price control, for example) have been temporary and have been dropped as soon as an emergency has passed. But many others have continued and expanded.

For example, the first big impetus to grades and standards for farm products in the United States came during World War I. But since then the program has grown much larger. Then in the late 1920's and the 1930's, agricultural surpluses led to a variety of governmental programs aimed at raising and stabilizing the prices of farm products. Although these programs have changed a great deal, they are still very active —not only in the United States, but in most agricultural countries. Again, World War II, and food relief after that war, resulted in many international food marketing programs. Today national governments have a good deal to say about amounts to be imported and exported, and especially about prices of farm products in international trade. This may, or may not, prove to be a temporary trend. But clearly the trends since World War II have not been toward free international trade in farm products; rather, they have been toward government controls and subsidies of various kinds (usually under some more acceptable name).

Should we have more, or less, governmental activity in agricultural marketing? And could some of the present marketing programs be made more useful without increasing their size and cost?

Here we get into very controversial matters. Some citizens firmly believe that governmental programs in agricultural marketing have gone too far and should be curtailed. Other citizens believe just as firmly that these programs should be broadened and strengthened. This is part of an ancient controversy about economic policy generally. It is a controversy that you cannot avoid if you are to do your duty as an intelligent citizen and voter. Still less can you avoid it if you should become a Congressman, or a bureaucrat who administers one of the agricultural marketing programs.

We shall not try to give you an authoritative answer to the controversy. You will have to find your own answer—just as you will have to cast your own vote. But we do hope that this part of the book will help you form your own judgments. To be an intelligent voter, bureaucrat, or Congressman, you will have to think for yourself. You can't rely upon slogans and other substitutes for thought. Thinking is often hard work. To think straight about agricultural marketing programs, you will need facts and economic theory. We hope that Part 4 will give a fair sample of the kinds of facts and theories that will be useful in studying a wide variety of governmental policies affecting the marketing of farm products.

In a democratic country, the government is the people. Ideally, at least, it does what the majority of the people want. Thus, the aim of any marketing program of any governmental agency should be to benefit the public—that is, all the people.

This aim of government programs is broader than the aims of the programs discussed up to this point. Previously we discussed how an individual, a firm, or a co-operative association could benefit members of their own industries. These aims are good, sound, desirable. But all civilized nations have found that the programs of individuals, and of industries, are not enough. They need to be supplemented by various kinds of services, regulations, and programs by government.

Part 4 will discuss several kinds of marketing programs carried on by government. We emphasize that the aim of such programs should be to protect and benefit the whole public. This is sometimes forgotten, even in government agencies. We like to recall the words of Abraham Lincoln, who said in 1864, "The Agricultural Department . . . is peculiarly the people's Department, in which they feel more directly concerned than in any other." This is a good thought to remember when someone says that the United States Department of Agriculture is not a "welfare agency." All departments of the government should be welfare agencies, not just agencies to help special interest groups.

Perhaps this seems a trifle academic. Let's get down to cases. Take the problem of food grades. Who should decide whether we are to have government food grades, and, if so, how they should be defined? Certainly, farmers have a stake in this problem; so do processors, both large and small; and so do retailers—chains and independents. The trade associations have a right to be heard. But all these voices represent special interests. The most important voice of all is that of the consumer. Unfortunately, this voice sometimes is not heard very distinctly. But do not forget that the consumer is the key to profitable marketing. In fact, he *is* the market. Whether we are considering food grades or any other marketing problem, we shall be wise to study what the consumer wants. We should consider this just as seriously as we do the more vocal demands of producers and of industry groups.

20

What Minimum Standards?

Here we are concerned only with official standards, developed and administered by some agency of the government. Of course, individuals and groups often have standards of their own. The old guilds made, and enforced, their own standards. Modern corporations and co-operatives do somewhat the same thing. But all civilized countries have found that such individual and group standards are not enough—that they must be supplemented with basic standards that are determined, and enforced, by the government. It is these government standards that we shall consider here.

Standard Measures

Man could never have progressed beyond simple barter without commonly accepted standards of measurement. As a practical matter, these standards are determined by governments throughout the world. They include standards of length (foot, meter); standards of weight (pound, gram); and standards of volume (bushel, quart).

These, and many other, standards of measurement are so obviously essential to modern marketing that we often take them for granted. But they are still important, and the problems in this field are not all solved. Federal, state, and local governments find it necessary to make frequent checks to prevent short weights, for example. Among the town officials in New England are the Sealer of Weights and Measures and the Measurer of Cordwood. They still have work to do. And an important function under the Federal Packers and Stockyards Act is to check the accuracy of livestock weighing.

Back in the 1920's, one of the lively issues was that of standard containers. At that time, farmers in different parts of the country used a great variety of containers. Some of them held such odd amounts as ⅞ of a bushel, or even ¹⁵⁄₁₆ of a bushel. The old Bureau of Agricultural Economics was instrumental in gradually eliminating many of these odd sizes. As a result, we have come to use only a rather small number of standard containers. So this problem has become less important—and less controversial. Yet there are still many problems in this field. One of them is the conflict between standards of volume and standards of weight. The nature of this conflict is indicated by the following quotation from an old *Webster's Dictionary* (1847):

> "*Bushel:* a dry measure containing . . . . 2150.42 solid inches, equivalent to 1131 ounces and 14 pennyweights troy."

But what if 2150.42 cubic inches of wheat, or of potatoes, do not weigh what Noah Webster said they should? Is a bushel 2150.42 cubic inches? Or is it 1131 ounces and 14 pennyweights troy? The general trend seems to be toward sale by weight rather than by volume. But many farm products can be sold most conveniently in standard containers. Strawberries, for example, can be handled best in baskets of one quart or one pint. Some states, and some cities, sporadically try to enforce weight regulations on strawberries. But some varieties, from some areas, may run light in weight. It may be impossible to jam in enough berries to meet the weight requirements without ruining them.

Standards of Purity and Health

Most of us in the United States now take the Pure Food and Drug laws for granted. These laws protect us from food that is adulterated, spoiled, or otherwise unhealthful. We don't like rat droppings in our wheat or too much spray residue on our apples. And it takes constant vigilance to give us the protection we need. Our milk is subject to all kinds of local inspection to keep down the bacteria count and to see that pasteurization is adequate to kill the bacteria that gets into the milk in spite of rigid barn inspection.

Perhaps we sometimes overdo this business of sanitation and purity. Perhaps we sometimes adopt regulations that are more effective in raising costs, or in reducing competition, than in protecting health. This may be especially true in the case of some local milk programs, under which the city authorities may refuse to inspect dairies that lie outside the present milk shed. The misuse of health regulations as a trade barrier can hardly be condoned.

Many less developed countries urgently need more effective programs of food sanitation, purity, and health. They need some system of frequent and adequate inspection. Such inspection is not to punish the wicked middleman. Rather, it is to protect the consumer—and thus to promote trade. In the long run, a sound program of food inspection greatly benefits farmers and middlemen, as well as the consumer, by increasing mutual confidence in the conditions of trade.

Standards of Truth and Honesty

Any kind of misrepresentation harms trade. It makes the consumer dissatisfied and suspicious. It would be impossible to draw up a set of regulations to forbid every possible specific case of misrepresentation. Rather, we have such agencies as the Federal Trade Commission with broad authority to investigate particular cases and to make rulings. The F.T.C. has plenty of business in foods, clothing, and tobacco products. Even so, some of us are a little suspicious of the claims made in some of the cigarette advertising, for example. We may wonder about all these "independent research laboratories" that prove that Alfalfa Cigarettes make your teeth "up to 76.2 per cent brighter"—or similar claims that are not exactly wrong, but that are certainly meaningless and probably misleading.

Costs and Returns

Standards may be set too low or too high. They are too low if they do not give the consumer adequate protection. They are too high if they require such costly methods of production and marketing that the price of food is raised unduly—or that the net price to the farmer is depressed unduly.

The "law of diminishing returns" applies to standards and to inspection—as well as to the production of wheat or milk. The higher the standards, the greater the cost of meeting them. Someone must pay the higher cost. In the long run, the consumer probably pays most of them. And this is obviously proper—assuming that the standards are solely for the protection of consumers. But if standards are made too fancy and too expensive, a point will be reached where further frills will do more harm than good.

Suppose, for example, that still more stringent inspection of dairy herds reduced the average bacteria count by, say, 10 per cent, but that it increased the retail price of milk by 2 cents a quart. Would babies gain or lose from the more expensive standard? The babies in the poorest families might well be worse off, because their parents might not be able to pay more for milk.

This is only one of hundreds of examples. The standards for any farm product affect costs, prices to consumers, and returns to farmers. The economics of standards has been given scant attention. We hope some reader of this book may feel the urge to explore this field of work. It is not only one that has great practical importance, but one that will challenge the best brains of competent economists. It is also a peculiarly difficult field of work for the economist. The technicians and health officials do not always understand the economist's analysis of standards. They may suspect that he is willing to "compromise between adequate health standards and cost." They may even denounce him for being willing to "sacrifice the lives of little babies to save a few dollars." These are misunderstandings. First, all standards must compromise between perfection and cost. No one could afford such close control over milk that not a single bacterium could be found. Second, the economist likes little babies, too. But he notes that babies can be harmed by unsanitary milk and also by no milk at all. He asks the difficult but certainly legitimate question: where should the standards be set so that most families can afford to buy adequate amounts of milk that are reasonably safe? The word *reasonably* means a compromise, but this is inevitable.

QUESTIONS FOR DISCUSSION

1. What advantages to trade are there in standardization?
2. List ways in which standards can be misused.

SUPPLEMENTARY READING

1. Gordon, Leland J., *Economics for Consumers.* New York: American Book Company, 3rd ed., 1953, Ch. 24.
2. Hoyt, E. E., *Consumption in Our Society.* New York: McGraw-Hill Book Company, Inc., 1938, Ch. X.
3. Kitchen, C. W., "Standardization and Inspection of Farm Products," *Yearbook of Agriculture, 1940.* Washington, D.C.: U. S. D. A., p. 667.
4. "Marketing," *Yearbook of Agriculture, 1954.* Washington, D.C.: U. S. D. A., pp. 142-169.

21

How to Define Grades

Someone, or some agency, has to decide what is a U. S. No. 1 potato, a choice carcass of beef, a middling bale of cotton, and a lot of B3F burley tobacco.

Many years ago, such decisions were made by individual producers, by processors, or by trade associations. Now they are almost entirely made by governmental agencies—at least, in the most advanced nations. The United States Department of Agriculture, for example, has defined grades for all the principal farm products grown in the country.

But the job of defining grades is not done once for all time. Grade definitions must be reviewed periodically to see if changes are needed.

On what basis should grades be defined? And how can a government expert determine whether present definitions should be changed?

What Are "Grades"?

We have previously discussed standards of weights and measures, which facilitate trade; and standards of purity, which protect the health of consumers. Grade standards are still another kind. They are intended to differentiate different lots of a commodity according to relative quality, over and above the minimum for health standards.

Grade standards provide a common language for buyers and sellers in arriving at prices. This is important where relevant quality characteristics cannot be immediately judged just by looking at the product. It is even more important in transactions by telephone or telegraph, in which the buyer cannot personally inspect what he is buying. It is important in other types of transactions, too, such as the extension of credit against commodities as collateral. A great deal of modern agricultural marketing depends upon governmentally established quality standards and grade certification by official inspectors.

But what is "quality"? Farm products have many different qualities, desirable or undesirable, or desirable in some uses but not in others. Some types of wheat make good bread flour; others are better for making macaroni-type products. Some kinds of potatoes are good for boiling but not so good for baking or for making potato chips. Which kind a buyer will prefer depends upon the use he intends to make of them.

Modern technology is multiplying the number of such special characteristics that suit products to specific uses. It is helpful to have potatoes identified as bakers or boilers or chippers in marketing, or to have wheats distinguished as bread wheats or those for making alimentary pastes. But these are not "quality" characteristics for purposes of setting grade standards, because they are not factors of *general* preference.

Dirt on potatoes, or in wheat, on the other hand, is undesirable in any use. All buyers prefer—and will pay something extra to have—potatoes that are free from dirt. Buyers generally also prefer eggs that hold together rather than run all over the frying pan, or canned peaches that have been carefully peeled. It is characteristics of this type, that have general market preference and, hence, a stable association with market value, that determine "quality" in the sense that we are concerned with in grade standards.

The Economic Principle

We believe that a system of grades for any farm product should be based solely upon existing market preferences. The economic measure of preferences is the price that buyers are willing to pay when they have a choice between different qualities. Suppose we are to set up three grades for some farm product. We should put in the top grade those qualities which normally sell at the highest price. We should put in the middle grade those qualities which sell at medium prices.

We should put in the lowest grade those qualities that sell at the lowest price.

This simple principle is not fully accepted by everybody. Some would base the grade definitions (in part, at least) upon nutritional characteristics. Some would rely heavily upon the preferences of technical experts rather than upon the preferences of the general public as expressed in the market. We do not agree with these views and shall give our reasons briefly.

First, what about nutrition? We grant, of course, that foods should be nutritious. Certainly the consumer should be protected against food that is contaminated, adulterated, or harmful in any way. Certainly he has a right to know that the foods he buys meet reasonable standards of nutrition. But, as we see it, this is not a problem to be handled by grades. Rather, it is a problem to be handled by minimum standards for pure foods. This was discussed in Chapter 20. In general,

Courtesy U.S.D.A.

A.M.S. official sizing device is used for checking size of potatoes.

it is unlawful to sell any foods that are harmful or that fail to meet minimum standards of nutrition. Thus, all foods that are sold legally are wholesome and nutritious.

But not all nutritious food is equally desirable. The housewife dislikes potatoes that are small and that have many cuts and bruises. They are just as nutritious as medium-sized potatoes that are without blemishes, but they make more work in the kitchen and they make more waste. Some housewives are glad to buy small, bruised potatoes if the price is low enough. But if they pay premium prices, they insist upon medium sizes and upon sound potatoes with little waste. Again, consumers want tender beef, even though tough beef may be just as nutritious. They want bright-colored apples, and butter with a mild flavor. These preferences are basic and deep-seated.

The preferences of the average consumer may have little relation to nutrition. Also, the likes and dislikes of the general public may differ from those of the "expert." Take the color of apples. Without doubt, the general public strongly prefers apples that are highly colored. Many experts—professors of pomology, for example—have argued that the color of an apple skin is no indication of quality. They have said that some of the best-tasting apples are dull in color. And they have pointed out that many highly colored apples are rather tasteless. In other words, they have contended that the public's preference for highly colored apples is really a prejudice based upon ignorance. They may well be right.

But it is an elementary principle of marketing that successful grades must be based upon the existing preferences (or prejudices, if you wish) of the general public. When the average housewife buys Number 1 Grade apples, she expects them to be highly colored. She is the one who must be pleased —not the nutritionist or the pomologist with the educated taste. When Mrs. Jones pays a premium price for a Choice grade beef steak, she expects it to be tender. The beef grades would soon break down if we allowed tough beef in the top categories.

The tastes and preferences of the general public may be

uneducated and irrational. If so, someone should try to change them. But this is a job for educators, not for the bureaucrats who have to define grades. Moreover, don't be too sure that the preferences of the public are irrational. After all, is it irrational to want a bright-colored apple? Is taste necessarily more important than color? And what tastes are best? Do consumers buy apples to get nutrition, or simply because they like apples?

Quality Improvement

Colleges and governmental agencies have worked long and hard to improve the quality of farm products. They have shown farmers how to produce better cotton, milk, and potatoes. They have developed methods of handling and transporting to maintain quality during the marketing process.

The aim of this work may seem perfectly clear. But is it really? What is quality improvement? Is the aim for everyone to produce the highest possible quality? We think not. Take potatoes, and consider only one quality factor: bruises. The most careful farmer bruises a few potatoes when he digs them. The best storage-housemen bruise a few. Even with careful handling, some potatoes are bruised in transit and in the retail store. It would be ridiculous to try to prevent every single bruise. Farmers would have to pick up each potato with gloves, wrap it in a piece of velvet, and lay it gently in a box. Warehousemen, railroad employees, and retail clerks would have to go to similar extremes. To eliminate every last bruise would cost more than the potatoes are worth.

In other words, the principle of diminishing returns applies to quality control. Some farmers would find it profitable to produce goods of better quality. So would some middlemen. But some farmers and some middlemen have no doubt passed the point of diminishing returns. The extra income they get from producing a super-fancy quality does not cover the extra cost. There is no economic sense in preaching that everyone, everywhere, at all times, should produce better and better quality. Rather, the farmer or the middleman should seek the most profitable qualities to produce and sell, in the light of his own particular situation.

Let us look at this matter from the point of view of consumers, too. A few consumers are willing and able to pay premiums for superfine quality. The big mass of consumers want good quality at a moderate price. And some consumers with low incomes are glad to get the lowest edible qualities at low prices. If we should produce and sell only the top grades, we would have to set the price so low that the poorest consumers could afford food. Or else we would have to feed them at public expense.

Most of economic life is a compromise. In adjusting the quality of foods, we must compromise between what the consumer wants and what farmers, processors, and dealers find profitable to supply. The classical economic theories about the allocation of resources would suggest that the general welfare is maximized when everyone produces those qualities that are most profitable. Of course, this assumes full knowledge and perfect competition. And perhaps the classical theory should be taken with a grain of salt, anyway. But it may serve as a general guide. For example, think of the several grades of wheat as several different commodities. How much of each should be produced and sold? Classical theory would say that the production of each grade should be carried just to the point where the expected market prices would equal the marginal costs. This is also the point of maximum profits to producers, processors, and distributors.

This problem of quality improvement (perhaps we should call it quality *adjustment*) can be solved only by considering both the economics of marketing and the economics of production. Marketing studies may discover how great a premium consumers will pay for eggs that have very small air cells. Studies of production economics may determine the necessary extra costs of reducing the size of air cells. These extra costs will vary from area to area, from farmer to farmer, from dealer to dealer. Some will find it profitable to produce and market eggs with very small air cells. Some will do better to produce and sell the medium or low grades.

More Than One Grade

In most cases, the farmer does not produce a single grade. The potato farmer, for example, produces all grades of potatoes. He may sort his crop into several grades, or he may sell it field run. The dealer may buy field-run potatoes and he may sort them by grade. What should be done with the lower grades? A popular notion seems to be that the lower grades should not be sold for human food—that they should not be allowed to compete with the higher grades. Such policies are followed under many of the fruit and vegetable marketing orders. Here is a problem in economics that calls for intensive study. We shall not try to give a definitive answer here. When supplies are plentiful and when prices are low, it may be good public policy to limit total shipments. The question raised here is whether such a limitation should always be applied to the lowest grades—allowing unlimited shipments of the higher grades. The authors of this book are doubtful that this is always the best policy—either for the farmer or for the consumer. If all grades will bring enough money to cover out-of-pocket costs, we have a problem calling for a rather elaborate theoretical and statistical analysis. So far as we know, such an analysis has not yet been made. Therefore, we withhold final judgment. But we have a tentative opinion that, in a situation such as we have described, it would be best to limit shipments of all grades—not just of the lowest grades.

Consumer Grades

We have argued that grades ought to be based entirely upon existing preferences of consumers. Of course, the final consumer (the housewife) does not buy many raw farm products. She is not in the market for wheat, cotton, leaf tobacco, or cattle. Rather, she buys bread, clothing, cigarettes, and beef.

The big bulk of our grading and inspection is on raw farm products. But there is a growing use of grades for foods bought by the consumer. The United States Government has established official grades for beef, eggs, canned fruits and vegetables, and butter. Some housewives can, and do, buy

Courtesy U.S.D.A.

A U.S.D.A. meat grader at work in the warehouse cooler. He judges the quality of the meat, according to U.S. standards, and applies the appropriate quality grade mark.

these foods by grade. For example, some stores sell beef that has been officially graded. The grade of this beef is stamped on the beef carcass. Officially graded eggs are identified on the carton.

None of these consumer grades are compulsory. It is entirely legal to sell these foods without designating the grade. Many stores do so.

From time to time there have been heated arguments about compulsory grade labeling. Many consumer organizations have long advocated such compulsory labeling. The most recent, and most bitter, arguments were in connection with the labeling requirements issued by the Office of Price Administration during World War II. The O.P.A. found that effective price control required grade labels for many items of food and clothing. But their regulations stirred up a hornet's nest of opposition from canners, other processors, and distributors. As a result, Congress denied the O.P.A. authority to require grade labeling.[1]

At present, there are no compulsory Federal grades for foods. There is a Federal act requiring that fabrics be labeled to show the percentages of raw wool, reworked wool, and other fibers. A few states require that all eggs be sold by grade. But, in general, the use of consumer grades is voluntary in the United States. They are used when, and if, the food trades find them to be profitable. Their use depends partly upon farmer push, but mainly upon consumer pull. That is, farmers generally like to have their products sold on the basis of grades, but are mainly interested in wholesale grades; millions of consumers want to buy products identified by grade, and they are not bashful about letting the food trades know their wishes.

We think that the arguments about compulsory grade labeling have generated more heat than light. For the present, the voluntary grades seem to be fairly satisfactory. They will keep on spreading if consumers want them strongly enough. But we are all consumers, and all of us over 21 years of age can vote. If we should some day vote for compulsory grade labeling of certain foods, the world probably would not come to an end. Nor would free enterprise and competition be doomed.

Anyway, the first question is how to define grades—whether they are voluntary or compulsory. In either case, retail grades will be useful only if they reflect the real preferences of consumers.

How can we find out what qualities of foods and clothing are preferred by consumers? Some preferences are obvious. It is easy to see that most consumers want lettuce to be fresh, not wilted. They prefer butter with a mild taste, not a strong flavor. They want bed sheets that will wear, not fall apart in a few months.

But such observations only give us a bare start. We need much more definite information as a basis for grade specifications. This calls for research.

---

[1] Meat grades were continued by order of the Office of Economic Stabilization.

QUESTIONNAIRES

One way to study consumer preferences is through questionnaire surveys. In some of the earlier studies, questionnaires were mailed to large numbers of families, asking detailed questions about their preferences. Typically, a large proportion of families failed to fill out the questionnaire and mail it back. Little attention was given to probability sampling in these studies. Also, sometimes the questions were so loaded as to invite an answer that might be misleading. In recent years, most preference surveys have been made by personal interviews. The sample of families has been carefully studied. The questions are usually framed carefully. Without doubt, the modern interview-surveys are more accurate than the old mail-surveys. The techniques of sampling, of interviewing, and of analyzing the data are improving greatly and rapidly.

EXPERIMENTS

Another approach to this problem is by experiment or demonstration. Even the best interviewer may not be able to find out your real preferences for lemon juice simply because you can't describe them accurately. But the researcher can experiment on you. He can get you to taste samples of lemonade. He may first discover that you cannot distinguish between samples that fall within a certain range of acidity. Then he may ask you which of two glasses of lemonade you prefer. You don't have to describe your preferences—you simply choose one class in preference to the other. Or the researcher may get several retail stores to co-operate in an experiment to see what sizes of potatoes are most preferred. Several sizes are put on display. The prices are changed from time to time during the experiment. A record is kept of the amounts of each size sold under each price situation. The customers of the store do not have to answer any questions. They vote with their dollars. The experimental technique has great possibilities.

Still another approach to this problem is a statistical analysis of price premiums and discounts paid in the ordinary markets for various qualities of food. Such studies can be made more easily in jobbing markets than in retail stores. The price variation from store to store often reflects not only differences in the quality of food, but also such things as differences in services and in markup policy. In the jobbing market, all retailers pay about the same price for the same quality. A researcher can make a detailed inspection of perhaps 100 different lots of tomatoes and can get sales records showing the prices paid for each lot. Then he can use multiple regression techniques to unscramble the data—that is, to measure the price differentials associated with differences in such characteristics as size, shape, color, maturity, and so on. This method has not been used much in recent years. In our opinion, it has some real advantages. In particular, it provides quantitative estimates of the net effects of various quality factors upon prices or price differentials.

The study of consumer preferences is a very important field for marketing research. Much progress has been made in recent years, but we still have far to go.

At present, the use of retail grades is restricted to a few commodities. Most of the foods and clothing bought by housewives are not identified by any official grades. Many items are identified by trademarks or brand names. A trademark, or a brand name, may help the consumer in many cases. Del Monte canned peaches, Swift's Premium hams, and Eight O'clock coffee are well-known to many consumers, who have learned to rely upon the quality of such trademarked items. But there are so many trademarked and branded items that many consumers are confused. Some of them, at least, would prefer a simple, uniform system of retail grades.

Perhaps our program of retail grades should be extended to more commodities; probably our terminology should be simpler and more uniform. Why not use such terms as "Grade 1," "Grade 2," and "Grade 3" in all cases?

Grades for Unprocessed Farm Products

The grades for cotton should no doubt reflect the preferences of the housewives who buy bed sheets, dresses, and other cotton goods. But they should also reflect some factors that may not concern the housewife directly. The cotton manufacturer naturally wants to buy the kinds of cotton that he thinks will be profitable to him. True, he wants those qualities of cotton that will make goods that satisfy consumers. But he also wants cotton that can be manufactured at low cost—for example, cotton that can be manufactured with little waste.

Similar considerations enter into the grade definition for wheat, leaf tobacco, and other farm products that are bought by processors and manufacturers.

QUESTIONS FOR DISCUSSION

1. What is the economic justification for grading?
2. How important is quality in the market, and how far should a producer go to attain quality produce?
3. What are the bases for consumer grades?

SUPPLEMENTARY READING

1. Brunk, Max E., and L. B. Darrah, *Marketing of Agricultural Products*. New York: Ronald Press Company, 1955, Ch. 17.
2. U. S. Department of Agriculture, "Grade Names Used in U. S. Standards for Farm Products," *Agricultural Handbook*, No. 157, December, 1958.
3. Waite, Warren C., and Harry C. Trelogan, *Agricultural Market Prices*. New York: John Wiley & Sons, Inc., 2nd ed., 1948, Ch. 12.

22

How to Regulate Rates

Under conditions of perfect competition, prices and rates for services would be determined by the process of bargaining between buyers and sellers. If there were such a thing as perfect competition, there probably would be little demand for government regulation of rates and of prices. But in actual economic life, competition is seldom, if ever, perfect. Often large concerns are able to exert powerful influences over market prices and rates for services. In any situation of this kind, either the farmer or the consumer is likely to feel that he is being unfairly exploited. This result is bound to lead to a demand for some sort of public regulation.

Even if it were desirable, it would hardly be possible for the government to regulate all prices and rates charged by all businesses. On what basis, then, can we decide which rates and which prices to regulate? One popular notion is that the decision should be made on the basis of the size of firms in an industry. According to this idea, any concern doing more than a stated amount of business in a year would be subject to regulation. Another form of this proposal is that any industry would be regulated if the four or five largest concerns did more than, say, 75 per cent of the business.

This approach would be fairly easy to apply. But any simple, statistical procedure of this kind misses the main point. When does the farmer need protection? When there is evidence that powerful buyers are holding the price down below its normal level. When does the consumer need protection? When there is evidence that powerful sellers can raise the retail price of a commodity. The test, as we see it, is not how many buyers and sellers there are. Rather, it is how they act. Even though there are only three or four actual buyers in an area, they may compete vigorously with one another, paying the farmer full value and keeping their margins as low as possible. Yet one hundred buyers or sellers in some industry— although technically independent—might follow a single leader, develop the market between them, or conspire with one another to fix prices.

In general, prices and rates should not be regulated by government agencies unless the cost of regulation is less than the injury that might be done to farmers and consumers without such regulation.

This chapter will discuss only the regulation of freight rates. But the same principles apply in some degree to the regulation of other rates.

What Level of Freight Rates?

Most areas are served by only a few railways or waterways. These methods of transport must meet competition by motor truck. But, aside from that, they are natural monopolies. It would be quite impractical to have two or more railways or two or more waterways competing for business at each shipping point. Unless rates were regulated, railways and waterways could set almost any rates within wide limits. The lower limit would be marginal cost, or what is often called "out-of-pocket cost." In the case of railways and waterways, the marginal cost is ordinarily small in relation to total costs. The upper limit of freight rates is what is euphemistically called "the value of the traffic." Another phrase for it is "what the traffic will bear." The railway or waterway will not want to set its rates so high that it loses all the business to its competitors, such as motor trucks.

Obviously, no regulatory agency would want to set any freight rate below marginal cost. Ordinarily, the agency will consider not only marginal costs, but also a fair return on investment and a normal profit. However, neither the regulatory agency nor the railroad can ignore competition. A railroad may find it advantageous to lower its rate for hauling feed grains, for example, in order to keep its traffic from competitors, even though the present rate may not fully cover all costs. The regulatory agency will, in many cases, find it advisable to allow such competitive rates.

Rate Discrimination May Be Preferable

Many people have advocated a simple structure of freight rates based solely upon costs. One common proposal is a standard rate per ton-mile. A slightly less simple rate structure would vary with the distance hauled but would charge all commodities the same rate for the same distance. Such proposals have two appeals. First, they would substitute a simple structure for the present complicated and bewildering one. Second, they would eliminate most of the present discrimination which seems unfair to many people.

However, some degree of discrimination in freight rates appears necessary to meet the actual conditions of competition. A nondiscriminatory rate structure would force railroads and waterways to give up a good deal of traffic that is actually profitable to them because it more than covers their marginal costs.

Although some kinds and some degree of rate discrimination seem practically inevitable, the regulatory agency naturally must keep a watchful eye upon this process to make sure that there are not too many arbitrary and capricious differences in rates that may distort production and marketing by encouraging production in uneconomic areas and discouraging it in areas that have natural advantages.

Carriers prescribe their own rates, and the Interstate Commerce Commission requires that the rates be just and reasonable. This, however, does not close the door on discrimination. It can be argued that the cost and revenue picture for a carrier is best measured for the total firm rather than by individual commodities. The reduction of some rates for economic reasons means that other sources of revenue must be found to meet overhead costs and provide a return on capital investment.

Commodity Rates

Much agricultural traffic moves under class rates applying to large groups of commodities. This fact reduces the number and size of the freight tariffs which have to be published. Under this system, commodities are identified under classes and the class rate applies to the commodity. There is, however, another method of rating known as *commodity rates*. Individual commodities receive individual rates developed according to the market for that particular freight. This method allows for discrimination and an increase in rates where the demand for transportation is inelastic or a decrease in commodity rates when justified by particular conditions. These rates for railroads are available in published form at the local or regional level in accordance with regulations of the Interstate Commerce Commission.

Regional Discrimination

Under conditions of perfect competition, the price at which a product is sold reflects costs of transportation. These, in turn, vary with the distance between the market and the producer. The price will increase by the cost of transportation. Where the rates for long hauls fail to cover additional costs related to mileage, distant producers are given an advantage, and vice versa. The ability of transport agencies to adjust rates could readily change the competitive position of one region relative to another or of one locality relative to another. For example, if the freight rates for poultry feed were raised from the Midwest to Georgia and lowered for shipments to New England, the competitive status of the two areas would obviously be changed. Railroads may be interested in the development of particular industries on their own rail lines. Manipulation of rates to levels lower than would be justified if cost increased with distance will provide producers with markets not previously available to them. The reduced rates enable them to compete with firms on local markets. The agricultural development of the West was encouraged by rate reductions for westward-bound manufactured goods and for eastward-bound agricultural products.

Transit Privileges

Transit privileges may take the place of rate reductions as a form of discrimination. Milling in transit provides a continuation of the local rate on grain to its final destination as flour after being milled at some intermediate point. This arrangement enables millers to locate at lower-cost points between the point of origin of the grain and the market for the flour. If this were not so, millers would be located at higher-cost points of consumption in order to take advantage of the lower rates provided for grain. Carload rates may be the same as or lower than less-than-carload rates. This relationship will determine the location of jobbers. If carload rates are lower, then jobbers who can ship by carload lots will gain the business. This, in general, would favor jobbers located close to large consuming areas. Less-than-carload rates may also be used to meet competition from rival forms of transportation.

Competition Between Types of Transportation

The increase in truck transportation brought on by improved roads and trucks, as well as by the increased demand for transportation, has increased the competition between various forms of transit. Not only are trucks being substituted for railways, but the airplane and waterway provide additional competition. The competition is expressed in rates and in services. The speed and convenience of air travel are compared with the slower boat and railroad in relation to market needs. The lower rate offered on waterways will not attract those commodities that must be moved rapidly for sale. A commodity such as potatoes may adopt any of these means of transport, but the final price at which the potatoes can be offered for sale will depend on the unit cost of transportation. Therefore, under competition, the form of transport will be used that offers the lowest rate and yet provides that service that will meet the market requirements.

Railroad rates have always been affected by the alternative waterway routes available. Shipments from New York to Memphis, Tenn., for example, could be made by boat to Savannah, Ga. and by rail to Memphis, or by rail to St. Louis and from St. Louis by rail to Memphis. A rail rate charged from New York to St. Louis or from St. Louis to Memphis would recognize the competitive water rate from New York to Savannah. Rates where water competition is impossible could be raised to carry losses on other lines. This type of compensation has encouraged control of more than one railroad under the same management.

Discrimination Justified

Where such controls were possible, railroads have had to subsidize low-rate hauls. Without subsidy, certain lines would probably have slowly depleted their capital reserves and have gone out of business. Internal subsidy by a rail company has permitted services to be maintained that would otherwise have been discontinued. Nevertheless, it would be subject to abuse without governmental control, provided in part by the Interstate Commerce Commission.

Who Pays the Freight?

The freight is normally included in the price paid by the consumer. A product priced at $1.00 in Des Moines, Iowa with shipping charges of 25¢ will sell at $1.25 in Chicago. If it will not sell at this price, either the price at Iowa or the freight charges must be reduced. A decline of freight charges to 20¢ would allow sale in Chicago at $1.20. If there were a price-responsive market, changes in freight charges might make the difference between sale and no sale.

Given the demand curve DD in Figure 12 and the supply curve SS for a commodity, the equilibrium price will be at P. Now let us assume an increase in the freight rate. Producers will no longer be willing to produce L if the market price is P. They will now need a market price of P'' (that is, $P +$ freight) to induce them to keep on producing L. The new supply curve RR increases the equilibrium market price to P'

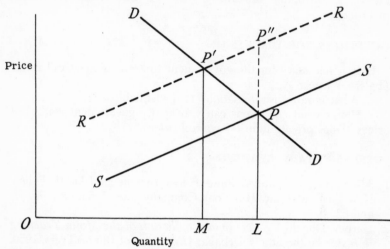

Figure 12.

at a reduced supply of *OM*. The market price is raised from *P* to *P′* But this is not enough to cover the increase in freight rate. Ordinarily, the increase in freight rates will be borne partly by farmers, in terms of lower prices at the farm, and partly by consumers, in the form of higher market prices.

The final burden of freight rates is a very complicated matter. For example, an increase in freight rates would not affect all farmers in the same way. Farmers who are near the consuming market may actually gain some advantage if their distant competitors have to pay higher rates. This is especially true when it becomes necessary to grant a general percentage increase in all freight rates. Since World War II there have been many such general increases. They have been allowed in order to cover increased costs of labor and materials. Without question, some increases in freight rates have been necessary in recent years. It is important to remember, however, that all such broad changes in freight rates may very substantially affect interregional competition. The changes may not be too severe if an increase in freight rates comes when demand is high and when all market prices are increasing. But a general increase in freight rates on farm products when demand is stationary or falling may be disastrous to distant producers.

QUESTIONS FOR DISCUSSION

1. Is it necessary for the government to regulate: (a) rail rates? (b) truck rates?
2. What is rate discrimination? Is it justifiable?
3. Under what conditions can you justify government control of prices? Does private industry control prices?

SUPPLEMENTARY READING

1. Allen, Buchanan, and Colberg, *Prices, Income, and Public Policy.* New York: McGraw-Hill Book Company, Inc., 1954, Chs. 30, 31, and 32.
2. Harper, Donald V., *Economic Regulation of the Motor Trucking Industry by the States.* Urbana: University of Illinois Press, 1959, Chs. 9 and 11.
3. Hudson, W. J., and James A. Constantin, *Motor Transportation.* New York: Ronald Press Company, 1958, Ch. 23.
4. Meyer, J. R., M. J. Peck, *et al., The Economics of Competition in the Transportation Industries.* Cambridge, Mass.: Harvard University Press, 1959, Ch. 1.

23

What Storage Operations

We are concerned here with storage by government rather than by private industry.

Private industry stores farm products in the hope of making profits. The farmer who stores apples in the fall does so because he expects the price to go up enough during the winter and spring to pay all storage costs and leave a profit. In a similar way, the egg merchant in Chicago buys in the spring when prices are low in hopes that prices will go up enough so that he can sell them at a profit in the fall. These are examples of seasonal storage. Practically all seasonal storage is done by private industry, including farmers, co-operative associations, and dealers of various kinds. In addition to seasonal storage, substantial amounts of staple farm products are commonly carried over from one crop year to another. Until about 25 years ago these operations, too, were carried out mainly by private industry. In recent years, however, many governments have undertaken considerable responsibility for holding rather large stocks of farm products for considerable periods of time—often, for several years.

The aims of government storage are not the same as the aims of private industry. Government storage might be intended to accomplish any one or more of the following purposes:

1. To prepare for possible military emergencies.
2. To safeguard against shortages, such as those due to weather.
3. To reduce the violence of fluctuations in farm prices and incomes.
4. To raise farm prices and incomes.

To Prepare for Possible Military Emergencies

Countries that import substantial amounts of food and fiber are especially vulnerable to modern warfare. Their food and fiber imports might be almost completely shut off for considerable periods of time. For this reason, many governments have found it advisable to stockpile such farm products as wheat, cotton, and wool.

This factor is not so important in the case of the United States except for wool, sugar, and possibly rubber. Except for these commodities, our military problem is not so much the safeguarding of imports. Rather, it is the storage of adequate food supplies for our own civilian population. This is a big problem, but it is beyond the scope of this book.

To Safeguard Against Shortages

Warfare causes sudden changes in demand for farm products. The weather sometimes causes sudden changes in crop yields. Government storage operations can be justified not only as a means of providing for unusual military needs, but also as a safeguard against unusual weather conditions that might result in food shortages.

There is nothing new in this idea. The Bible tells how Joseph stored grain in the seven fat years and distributed it in the seven following lean years. Presumably he helped prevent serious starvation in Egypt. This same idea has been revived from time to time. A recent example is the discussion of international reserves for famine relief.

Here we are concerned not so much with international aspects of storage as with national policy. If governments are to be responsible for holding sizable stocks of food for several years, they need some guide as to the quantities that are needed or desirable. In principle, this should be a fairly simple matter. If the purpose is to be prepared to meet possible low yields due to weather, we should be able to find out how much variation in yields we have had in the past and how much can be expected in the future. A study of this kind was made in the United States in 1952.[1]

---

[1] Oris V. Wells and Karl A. Fox, "Reserve Levels for Storable Farm Products," Senate Document 130, Washington, D.C., 1952.

To Reduce Fluctuations in Farm Prices and Incomes

Farm prices and farm incomes are notoriously unstable. A short crop, or an unusual demand, or the threat of war may send prices skyrocketing. A bumper crop or a business depression may force farm prices and farm incomes to disastrously low levels.

This situation makes farming a hazardous occupation. Moreover, a depression in agriculture, if prolonged, may spread to other parts of the economy. When their prices and incomes are low, farmers buy less farm machinery and less fertilizer and even reduce their purchases of goods for family living. Thus, extreme fluctuations in farm prices and farm incomes may be harmful to the whole economy. This doesn't mean that we accept the doctrine that all wealth originates in agriculture and that all depressions originate in agriculture. But we do believe that government storage of farm products can introduce at least a degree of stability into the economy. We believe this to be one of the strongest arguments for such a course of action.

To Raise Farm Prices and Incomes

We have just discussed storage as a means of reducing fluctuations in prices and incomes. We must distinguish between the aim of stabilizing prices and that of raising prices. These two aims are commonly confused in public discussion of government programs.

Stabilization operations in themselves are not likely to raise the average level of farm prices and farm incomes very much.[2] Of course, farmers and Congressmen are pleased when the government helps farmers keep surpluses off the market by non-recourse loans or by actual purchases. The immediate effect of such a program is to strengthen market prices. But neither farmers nor Congressmen are usually so pleased when government stocks are sold in the open market. The sale of

---

[2] Geoffrey S. Shepherd, *Agricultural Price and Income Policy*. Ames: Iowa State College Press, 1952.

These twin elevators add 13 million bushels to the grain storage capacity of the Chicago area. The elevators were erected by the Chicago Port Authority at Lake Calumet Harbor. One is leased to the Rice-Powell Grain Company; the other to the Illinois Grain Corporation. Both elevators can load grain into or out of ships, barges, rail cars or trucks.

stocks tends to reduce prices. Government storage is not a way of permanently reducing market supplies. Rather, it is a way of reducing market supplies in years of large crops and increasing market supplies in years of small crops.

How Stabilization Affects Farmers and Consumers

Stabilization may raise or lower farm income. It may benefit or harm the consumer. Its effect depends partly upon the shape of the demand curve and partly upon the level at which prices are stabilized.

Figure 13 illustrates the essential principles.

The diagram shows two possible demand functions for a commodity. The line *DD* illustrates the case of a linear demand function. The dotted curve *dd* illustrates the case of a curvilinear function. In both cases we assume that, in the

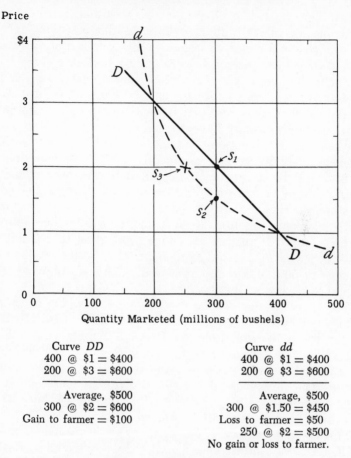

Figure 13. Stabilization: Effects upon Farmer and Consumer.

absence of stabilization, market supplies fluctuate between 400 million bushels and 200 million bushels. In both cases we assume that when the supply is 400 million bushels, the market price is $1; and that when market supplies are 200 million bushels, the price is $3. Thus, both demand curves indicate that if supplies alternate between 400 million bushels one year and 200 million bushels the next, the average farm income would be 500 million dollars.

When it comes to the effects of stabilization, however, the two demand functions give very different results. According to the linear demand function, it would be possible to sell

300 million bushels each year at $2 a bushel, resulting in a farm income of 600 million dollars. In this case (making no allowance for the cost of storage), the stabilization operation would raise farm income by 100 million dollars a year.

But if the true demand function were a curve, such as the dotted line, consumers would not buy 300 million bushels at $2 a bushel. Unless production were reduced, the stabilization operation would have to be carried on at the point marked s_2. At this point, farmers would sell 300 million bushels at $1.50, getting an income of 450 million dollars. This would be a loss of 50 million dollars a year from the average farm income of 500 million, even disregarding costs of storage.

To overcome this loss, farmers might try to reduce output. If they found it possible to reduce production to 250 million bushels a year, they could sell it at $2 a bushel, making an income of 500 million dollars a year, which is just what they would get with no stabilization.

The diagram also can be used to show how the consumer is affected by the stabilization of prices. Take, first, the case of the linear demand function DD and stabilization at $2 a bushel. Is the consumer better off with prices stabilized at $2 a bushel, or with prices varying from $1 to $3 in alternate years? The answer is that each individual consumer is at least as well off with prices fluctuating between $1 and $3 as he would be if prices were stabilized at $2.

This could be shown either in terms of "consumer surplus" or in terms of "indifference curves." In less technical detail, it can be demonstrated as follows. If prices were allowed to vary from $1 to $3, each individual consumer could, if he chose, buy exactly the same quantities that he would buy if the price were stabilized at $2. The cost of his purchases would be the same in either case. But when prices are allowed to fluctuate between $1 and $3, he has the choice of increasing his purchases in the low-priced year and reducing them in the high-priced year. But he will do this only if he finds it advantageous to do so.[3]

---

[3] The consumer, of course, cannot *know* that he is as well off unless he knows, when the price is $3, that this is to be made up to him next year by a price of $1. The analysis also neglects any cost he may be under from borrowing to finance his consumption in the high price years.

This same simple analysis applies to stabilization at point s_3 on the dotted curve. Any consumer is at least as well off with prices varying from $1 to $3 as he is with prices stabilized at $2.50.

On the other hand, each individual consumer would benefit if prices were stabilized at s_2 on the dotted curve. Suppose, for example, that an individual consumer bought four bushels a year when the price was $1 and two bushels a year when the price was $3. The cost for the two years would be $10. Now, if the price is stabilized at $1.50 a bushel, this consumer could, if he chose, still buy four bushels the first year and two bushels the second year. His total cost for the two years would now be $9 at the stabilized price. Moreover, the consumer could make a further gain by readjusting his purchases to the new price situation.

Thus, the effects of stabilization upon the consumer, as well as the effects upon the farmer, depend largely upon the level at which prices are stabilized. In general, farmers want stabilized prices at levels high enough to cover all costs of storage and leave them a net profit. This is, of course, a combination of two things: stabilizing prices and raising the average level of prices. In general, programs of this kind are not likely to benefit the consumer.

QUESTIONS FOR DISCUSSION

1. In a perfectly competitive market, what determines the amount of eggs stored in the spring for sale next fall? (or) the amount of feed grains held over from one crop year to the next?

2. What are the main arguments for and against storage operations by the government?

3. Do farmers benefit from storage operations, whether carried on by private industry or by the government?

SUPPLEMENTARY READING

1. Shepherd, G. S., *Agricultural Price Policy*. Ames: Iowa State College Press, 1947, Chs. 3 and 4.
2. Thomsen, F. L., *Agricultural Marketing*. New York: McGraw-Hill Book Company, Inc., 1951, Ch. 17.
3. Waite, Warren C., and Harry C. Trelogan, *Agricultural Market Prices*. New York: John Wiley & Sons, Inc., 2nd ed., 1948, Ch. 10.

24

Government Programs to Improve
Market Facilities

Governments throughout the world have concerned themselves with the improvement of marketing facilities.

The term *marketing facilities* includes all sorts of buildings, machinery, and equipment used in the marketing of agricultural products. It is obviously important that these facilities be adequate to handle the volume of products marketed. Also, it is important that they be properly designed and managed so that the marketing will be done efficiently. In democratic countries, at least, private trade has the major responsibility for providing and improving marketing facilities. However, even in the most democratic countries, governments are called upon to supplement the efforts of private industry.

Government agencies have often taken some responsibility for certain marketing facilities, especially when private industry was not in a position to provide them. Even in earliest recorded times, for example, most cities set aside a space for a public market where farmers and dealers could display and sell their goods. Today many governments find it necessary to go considerably farther than this.

Why Do Inefficient Facilities Persist?

One of the virtues usually claimed for competition is that it eliminates inefficiencies. Yet, it is not hard to find many examples of inefficient processing plants and distributing facilities. Their existence is due in part to ignorance. It is probably also due in part to the fact that large sums of money have been invested in obsolete facilities and that the investors resist any change that would lower the value of their investments.

Inefficient facilities have a habit of continuing for many decades or even centuries after they are outmoded. This is particularly true of city markets. Farmers and shippers wanting to sell in New York or Boston have no choice of market facilities. They must take whatever there is. Dealers on these markets have no choice, either. They, too, must use whatever facilities there are, even though they may be very inefficient. Both farmers and dealers would often like better marketing facilities, but they may not know just what is needed or how to get it.

Why do these situations persist? Why does not competition eliminate the inefficient facilities and methods? Perhaps competition would do this if allowed to work over a long enough period of time. But sometimes vested interests may obstruct competition. And often inefficient plants, both small and large, may continue to operate even though the return on investment may approach zero. Once the money is invested in a creamery or in a grain elevator, the owner is likely to run it if he can get any business at all. Until the thing begins to fall apart, society is stuck with it.

To continue to use a facility that has become obsolete, however, is not necessarily inefficient. If it is a specialized facility, and there is no other use for it, then the choice is between using it and junking it. As long as it can perform a marketing service as cheaply as a new, modern facility, with a return on capital based on its salvage or junk value, then the most economical course is to continue to use the facility. This would be the test of effective competition, at least in the short run.

It is the sort of test that is continuously faced by a plant manufacturing nuts and bolts, for example. It must sell its product as cheaply as competing plants do. If it cannot do this and make money, the owners soon find that they must modernize or close down.

But a city terminal market, for example, is not like a single nuts-and-bolts factory. It is a combination of many different plants and properties, owned or rented and operated by many different firms: receivers, wholesalers, jobbers, brokers, storage warehouses, railway lines, truckers, real estate companies, and numerous service and supply establishments, all inextricably interwoven. A new terminal cannot simply set itself up next door in competition with the old one. Modernization or relocation requires joint decision and joint action by many individuals. Each of them must be persuaded that he, or his firm, would benefit from the change. Some individual or group or agency must see the operation as a whole, envision the possibilities, develop comprehensive plans, and persuade those concerned of the benefits that could be achieved.

For 25 years or more, the United States Department of Agriculture has carried out an intensive campaign to help improve agricultural marketing facilities, working with state departments of agriculture and with land-grant colleges. This sort of work calls for a combination of research, education, and promotional efforts. The first task is usually to identify the factors causing inefficiencies. The second is to analyze alternative ways of overcoming the inefficiencies. The final one is to discover how to accomplish the changes.

State-Owned Markets, and Market Authorities

When the adoption of research recommendations is within the range of an individual firm, the manager has the option of adopting or rejecting the findings. When the research recommendations apply to market facilities in general, however, some concerted action by buyers and sellers using the facilities is necessary. In every large city of the United States, for example, there is a wholesale terminal market or district in which fruits, vegetables, meats, poultry, and other farm products are assembled for sale and distribution. Many of these markets are organized as private corporations. The users of the market rent facilities, and the market corporation is operated as a self-sustaining unit under central management. Some marketing facilities may be owned by farmer co-operatives and operated by a board of directors. The market facilities may be provided by the state. Florida and Georgia are two of the first states to operate farm assembly markets.

Other states have followed suit under state agricultural boards. Such boards acquire sites, erect marketing facilities for crops, livestock, or fruits and vegetables, operate warehouses and cold storage depots, and appoint a manager who hires the necessary staff. Such markets are not generally constructed where private market facilities are available. One Commissioner of Agriculture, for example, collects reasonable charges for use of the state-owned market facilities, has the authority

Courtesy U.S.D.A.

This first section of a Philadelphia wholesale food distribution center was opened in June 1959. In the completed 400-acre market, retail food dealers in the area can obtain a complete line of food directly from the warehouses, which will receive supplies by rail and truck from every state and many foreign countries.

to inspect crops coming into state markets, and has the power to declare an embargo on supplies competing with home-grown produce. He can establish and enforce minimum prices and quality standards for products.

South Carolina has a State Agricultural Marketing Commission which may appoint local market authorities at the request of twenty or more persons. Their duties include inspection, grading, and assistance in production practices, market practices, and financing. Buildings may be constructed or other facilities provided to form a market. Bonds, which are exempt from state and county taxes, may be issued and sold at public sale to finance the market. There are at least three regional market authorities in the State of New York, and in 1953 the Virginia State Legislature established a Produce Market Fund to provide capital for the construction of wholesale markets by market authorities. Numerous cities have market authorities with a commissioner to supervise the rules and regulations of location, traffic, sanitation, and so on.

The Needs

The establishment of market authorities under central control with the express purpose of providing facilities for improved buying and selling might go far in solving one of the basic problems of distribution in the less economically developed areas of the world.

There may be spots in any economy where inefficiency exists and where competitive forces are not adequate to provide a lower-cost remedy. There may be wasteful use of resources which could be remedied by some centralized action. Action by some government agency may be needed to provide these facilities, or at least to help private industry to provide them. In these cases, government is not competing with private industry. Instead, the government acts as a catalytic agent for encouraging and helping private industry to get the better facilities it needs and wants. The work of Mr. W. C. Crow and associates in the Agricultural Marketing Service is a good example of a combination of research, service, and promotion in co-operation with private industry.

The Federal subsidy of interstate roads has certainly improved the competitive position of the trucking industry. The old terminal facilities built for railroad distribution have proved too inflexible to meet changes in the size of cities and in residential developments. Gradually new market facilities are being built with the assistance of government specialists, by state funds or by co-operative action of interested traders. This has been brought on by the increased tempo of modern transportation and the need to maintain the speed and efficiency of long hauls to distributors at local levels. Some government assistance in providing improved marketing facilities is justifiable in terms of minimizing waste and spoilage, reducing costs, raising farm income, and improving the diets of consumers.

QUESTIONS FOR DISCUSSION

1. What do we mean by "market inefficiency"?
2. Name a type of inefficiency apparent to you in the handling and distribution of a food or food product.
3. Why do known inefficiencies persist? What could be done to hasten improvements?
4. Are there any limits to the participation of government in providing marketing facilities? Discuss.

SUPPLEMENTARY READING

1. Duddy, E. A., and D. H. Revzan, *Marketing*. New York: McGraw-Hill Book Company, Inc., 1947, Chs. 29 and 30.
2. Hoffman, A. C., and F. V. Waugh, "Reducing the Costs of Food Distribution," *The Yearbook of Agriculture, 1940*, pp. 627-637.
3. Stewart, Paul W., and J. F. Dewhurst, *Does Distribution Cost Too Much?* New York: Twentieth Century Fund, 2nd ed., 1948, Ch. 10.
4. Thomsen, F. L., *Agricultural Marketing*. New York: McGraw-Hill Book Company, Inc., 1951, Ch. 22.
5. *Marketing, Yearbook of Agriculture, 1954*. Washington, D.C.: U. S. D. A., pp. 36-59.
6. Abbott, J. C., "Marketing Policies and Improvement Programs," *FAO Marketing Guide* No. 1. Food and Agriculture Organization of the United Nations. Rome, 1958.

25

How to Dispose of Surpluses

The term *surplus* in this discussion will refer to supplies of agricultural produce that cannot be absorbed by the market in the form and at the prices required by existing market institutions. It is supply over and above demand at existing prices. Under perfectly competitive conditions, there could be no surpluses. Rather, when supplies were large, market prices would be depressed to the point where all the produce would be sold.

But price-support operations, if successful, prevent prices from falling to the competitive level. This means that some government agency must either buy part of the supply or lend the farmer money to keep it off the market. In either case, consumption is reduced. Also, if support prices are high, farmers may have an incentive to continue to produce more than can be sold in the regular market.

Problems of Disposal

With the continuation of such government price-support programs for the last two or three decades, the handling of surplus farm products apart from the normal market procedures has been a major problem of government. First, the holdings cannot be dumped on the market in periods of normal demand and supply without reducing prices and destroying the original objectives of the program. Second, the storage of such supplies apart from the normal market is expensive and, at best, only a temporary solution of the surplus problem. This has led to many programs intended to reduce surpluses.

Farmers have called on the government to do two things: *first*, to try to reduce output in line with market needs; and *second*, to dispose of such surpluses as were produced in spite of acreage allotments, soil banks, and marketing quotas. We shall not discuss production control here, except to note that we still have large surpluses after 25 years of government programs aimed at preventing them through production control. Here we are concerned with government programs to dispose of surpluses after they are produced. This problem is likely to be with us as long as the government supports the prices of farm products.

Chapters 11 through 14 discussed many forms of discriminative marketing by private concerns. When a private concern controls most of the supply of some product, a profitable policy may be to divert part of the supply to a secondary market, and to sell it there at a relatively low price in order to maintain a higher price in the primary market. But the practical possibilities of such programs by private industry are limited to cases in which a farmer co-operative or other large organization has almost complete control over market supplies.

Section 32

The government can, if it has legal authorities and funds for this purpose, buy the surpluses and dispose of them in various ways. Since 1935, it has had both the legal authority and the funds. Section 32 of Public Law 320 (as amended) appropriates an amount equal to 30 per cent of the customs revenues and makes it available to the Secretary of Agriculture to:

(1) encourage the exportation of agricultural commodities and products thereof by payment of benefits in connection with such exportation or by payments to producers in connection with the production of that part of any agricultural commodity required for domestic consumption;

(2) encourage the domestic consumption of such commodities or products by diverting them, by payment of benefits or indemnities or by other means, from the normal channels of trade and commerce or by increasing their utilization

through benefits, indemnities, donations or by other means, among persons in low-income groups as determined by the Secretary of Agriculture; and

(3) re-establish farmers' purchasing power by making payments in connection with the normal production of any agricultural commodity for domestic consumption.

Note how broad this authorization is. It authorizes almost any kind of surplus disposal except outright destruction.

One very effective way to dispose of surpluses would be to take them to the middle of the Atlantic Ocean and dump them. This would solve the storage problem. But disposition of food in this fashion would be contrary to the moral standards of Western civilization. The distribution system as provided by the market mechanism does not necessarily provide all consumers with their basic needs. Market demand is demand plus ability to pay. Without the ability to pay, demand has no economic significance, but it does have a moral significance. This extends to people in the United States as well as to people in economically less developed regions and countries. The struggle for survival that has marked the progress of man is closely related to the supply of food. The first of all productive activities is the provision of food and the storage of food between seasons. The wilful destruction of the products of agriculture in the name of economy would be accompanied by cries of indignation and shame even though in some cases it might be less expensive than a program to divert them to secondary uses. No politically conscious government will supplement its purchase programs with destruction programs. There have been a few well-advertised instances of destruction of surpluses because of spoilage or perishability of the product. But these instances are extremely rare.

Export Programs

Increased returns from the sale of surplus products without conflicting with commercial sales could be attained by export to the right market at the right time. A foreign market that would pay the domestic price for a commodity would be a profitable outlet. But where domestic prices are supported at levels higher than world prices, we cannot expect to export large amounts without some sort of price concessions to foreign buyers. Therefore, the sale of a surplus abroad will frequently mean a two-price system.

A higher price for domestic sales and a lower price for export sales, if feasible, may raise farm income. It will do so, for example, if the demand for an American product is inelastic on the domestic market and elastic on the foreign market. One disadvantage of this method is that other countries dislike being a dumping ground at times convenient for the exporter. The domestic production and normal trade of the importer are upset with repercussions on local producer prices and trading channels. The supply of dollars necessary for the purchase of imports must be obtained by the sale of exports to a dollar area or to the United States. This eventually means that the United States must import products from other countries, and this may be in conflict with established trade policy.

Another alternative of this scheme is to give the surplus to needy countries. This more costly method may have diplomatic significance that will return nonmonetary benefits to win the battle for freedom currently being waged between communist and non-communist peoples. In recent years the United States has sold large amounts of farm surpluses to foreign countries and has accepted foreign currencies in payment. This currency is held by the United States for purchases of supplies for defense or for other purposes. We also have bartered some of our surpluses in exchange for foreign products.

International Commodity Agreements

The disparity between United States and world prices as a result of the domestic price support programs has not only affected the surplus disposal programs but has also influenced the normal export markets. Texas cotton must compete with Egyptian cotton. United States wheat must compete with wheat from Australia and Canada. United States meat must compete with meat from the Argentine. To prevent the complete loss of export markets and to stabilize trade in wheat, the United States joined with major wheat-exporting countries and major wheat-importing countries in a wheat agreement. Under this agreement each supplying country agreed to export a minimum quantity priced within a range that the importing countries agreed to pay. This agreement went into effect immediately after World War II. The price at which the United States agreed to sell wheat was lower than the domestic price. In order to meet commitments under the agreement, the government has paid exporters the difference between the agreement price and the domestic support price.

Domestic Food Programs

In 1959 the United States Government was making surplus foods available to about 14 million school children and to about 7 million needy people in charitable institutions or family units. The surplus food used in these programs was donated by the Federal Government. Also, the government is authorized to pay certain costs of processing and packaging. Such programs not only can be of great benefit to those school children and needy families that get the surplus foods; they also can be an important outlet for food surpluses.

Shortly before World War II, the Federal Government operated a food stamp program through which needy families could buy foods at greatly reduced cost. The former food stamp program tried—probably with limited success—to concentrate the additional demand upon foods that were in surplus. In any case, the program probably succeeded in increasing the total food consumption of participating families. This not only improved the diets of these families; it also diverted some of the supplies from the regular market and helped to maintain the prices paid by nonparticipants.

In recent years there has been a revival of interest in various kinds of stamp proposals. Some of them would authorize a donation of surplus foods already held by the government. Others would be more like the former food stamp program in that participating families could buy any kind of foods through the regular grocery stores. These two kinds of programs are very different, both in their effects upon the consumer and in their effects upon farm prices and incomes. The big surpluses in the hands of the government are wheat, corn, and cotton. The donation of these commodities to needy families probably would not improve their diets. Moreover, it might well induce many needy families to buy substantially lower amounts of such products as meat, milk, and vegetables. Unless some way were found to insure that participating families maintained their normal commercial purchases of food, such a program might well actually reduce farm income.

The other type of food stamp program would be for the purpose of inducing participating families to increase their total food consumption. The greatest increases would doubtless be for meat, milk, vegetables, fruit, and similar foods that are needed in the diet. These are not foods that are now in the hands of the Commodity Credit Corporation. This kind of food stamp program would do little, if anything, for wheat, corn, and cotton. But it could do a great deal for livestock products, for example. A government program that would increase the market for livestock products would probably do more for farm income in the long run than a program to keep on subsidizing the surpluses of wheat, corn, and cotton.

Industrial Uses

Along with the current interest in food stamp plans, there is also a renewed interest in the possibility of using farm surpluses to make industrial products, such as alcohol, for example. This, of course, is not a new idea. The possibilities of "farm chemurgy" have interested many people, at least since the 1920's. Among those interested was Henry Ford.

The government has done a substantial amount of research to develop possible industrial uses of farm products. It operates several regional laboratories for this purpose. The laboratories have been successful in developing methods of using farm products for some industrial purposes.

Certainly there can be no question as to the merits of any industrial use that can pay the regular market price for farm products without any kind of subsidy. There is some question, however, about such programs as the diversion of potato surpluses into starch, alcohol, or animal feeds. In most cases these outlets for potatoes have not been able to pay anything like the market price. When they have been used as diversion outlets for large surpluses, they have required large government subsidies.

QUESTIONS FOR DISCUSSION

1. Under a "free market" there are no surpluses—everything is consumed at some price. Discuss this statement and its implications.
2. Is production control in agriculture feasible? Explain.
3. Diversion of surpluses into noncompetitive markets may raise farmers' incomes. It also costs somebody some money. Who pays for it? What do you think are the net gains or losses to farmers, to taxpayers, and to different groups of consumers?

SUPPLEMENTARY READING

1. Davis, J. H., "Surplus Disposal as a Tool for World Development," *Journal of Farm Economics*, Vol. XL, No. 5, December, 1958, pp. 1484-1496.
2. International Wheat Surplus Utilization Conference, *Proceedings*. Brookings, S. D.: Department of Economics, South Dakota State College, May, 1959.
3. Shepherd, G. S., *Agricultural Price Policy*. Ames: Iowa State College Press, 1947, Chs. 20, 21, and 22.

26

What Co-operation Between
Industry and Government

Part 3 of this book discussed industry programs. So far in Part 4 we have been discussing government programs. For many purposes it is convenient to make this distinction. However, in actual practice, most industry marketing programs require some participation by government, and most government marketing programs involve participation by industry. Thus, industry programs and government programs are not completely distinct things. One shades into the other.

For example, industry marketing programs may require some sort of government authority. They may also rely on government help for compliance. Thus, the marketing programs of the large farmer co-operative associations would be impossible without the legal authority granted by the Capper-Volstead Act. And most marketing agreements would be ineffective without government orders.

The reverse is also true. Government marketing programs are not run by a bunch of bureaucrats in Washington without advice and help from industry groups. Many of the Federal employees who administer these programs are recruited from industry. In addition, the administrators confer frequently with industry groups and often seek their advice before important changes are made in policies or in programs. Also, Congressmen and Senators often seek the advice of industry groups in developing new agricultural legislation. Lobbying has a bad name. But trade associations and farm groups often can perform a real service by helping Congressmen and administrators to develop workable programs.

Compulsory Co-operation

Back before World War II, several of the marketing schemes developed in British Empire countries were called "compulsory co-operation." This is, of course, a peculiar phrase. True co-operation must obviously be voluntary rather than compulsory.

However, many co-operative associations, both at home and abroad, have found that their marketing programs can have only limited success as long as even a small minority of the non-members refuse to participate. This is almost certain to be the case where a co-operative attempts to maintain a market price even slightly above competitive levels. In such cases, a small group of non-compliers is likely to wreck the program by price-cutting. To overcome these difficulties, some governments have attempted to strengthen the hands of the co-operatives by compelling all producers to comply with a program that has been accepted by a substantial majority.

These programs have taken different forms in different countries. But all of them have two features in common: first, the program is accepted by a large majority of the producers; and, second, some government agency supervises the program, enforces it upon all producers and dealers, and assumes responsibility for safeguarding the interests of consumers.

Marketing Agreements, Licenses, and Orders

In the 1920's and early 1930's, there was much discussion in the United States about various kinds of marketing agreements. This was the major feature of the proposals of George N. Peek to bring about what he called "equality for agriculture." E. G. Nourse,[1] writing about Mr. Peek's philosophy, said, for example, "It was evidently his belief that it was unwise or futile to attempt direct control or regulation of production, a general advisory role being all that should be attempted. He did, on the other hand, believe strongly that a substantial

---

[1] Edwin G. Nourse, *Marketing Agreements Under the A. A. A.* Washington, D.C.: The Brookings Institution, 1935, pp. 7 and 8.

enhancement of the farmer's income could be secured by marketing such supplies as did come forward under a co-ordinated administration sponsored and aided by the government."

This is the essence of the programs we have come to call marketing agreement programs and orders. They are operated under a co-ordinated administration sponsored and aided by the government. Somewhat similar programs were tried under the Federal Farm Board, which was authorized by the Agricultural Marketing Act of 1929. Following the failure of the Farm Board program, marketing agreements and licenses were authorized under the Agricultural Adjustment Act of 1933.

For a few years, while Mr. Peek was Administrator of the Agricultural Adjustment Administration, marketing agreements were a principal feature of the farm program. For example, in the years 1933–1935, the agreements and licenses covered not only fluid milk, fruits, and vegetables, but also evaporated milk, dry skim milk, rice, North Pacific wheat, tobacco, and a number of miscellaneous commodities, including honeybees and turpentine. Some of these were simple agreements with processors that they would pay some minimum price. When most of the processors agreed to such a provision, it could be enforced upon a minority by a system of licenses. Naturally, the license of any dealer could be suspended or revoked if he refused to comply.

After the first few years of the old A.A.A. program, the major emphasis was placed on attempts to control production. Marketing agreements, licenses, and orders continued but became much less important than Mr. Peek and his followers had in mind.

At the present time, marketing agreements and orders are authorized for milk and for certain fruits and vegetables, tobacco, soybeans, hops, honeybees, and naval stores. Moreover, the Agricultural Marketing Agreement Act of 1937, as amended, severely restricts the kinds of actions that can be taken under marketing agreements and orders. The milk marketing agreements and orders are limited primarily to setting up classified price plans with minimum prices to producers. Agreements and orders for other commodities may limit the total quantity marketed or the amount marketed of any grade or size, or it may involve rather elaborate schemes for diverting surpluses into lower-priced markets.

In general, these marketing agreement and order programs are developed jointly by industry groups and by the Department of Agriculture. No such program can be carried out without the express approval of the Secretary of Agriculture, who is responsible for safeguarding the interests of the public. However, these programs work best where they are supported by an active and organized group of producers. Thus, they have been successful in many local milk markets, especially where most of the producers are members of a strong cooperative. They have also worked well in the cases of certain specialty crops that are grown intensively in only a few, small areas.

Probably agreements and orders have helped to stabilize the prices of milk and of certain fruits and vegetables. There is some question as to whether these programs have actually raised prices and incomes over a period of time. At present, most of the milk marketing experts believe that the most successful marketing agreements have probably not affected the average price noticeably, but have been successful in ironing out some of the uneconomic fluctuations in prices and in marketing. Dr. Nourse, in the book mentioned above,[2] concluded:

> The more thoughtful among the proponents of "controlled marketing" argue that as this system develops and matures, it will demonstrate its ability to arrive at sounder decisions than would be reached through unco-ordinated action because it combines a maximum of free individual initiative and choice covering operative details for both producers and handlers with the necessary minimum of centralization on basic questions of marketing strategy. They point out also that the agency entrusted with these major decisions combines the intimate knowledge of producers and handlers as to the complex features affecting their individual businesses with the longer and broader

---

[2] Edwin G. Nourse, *Marketing Agreements Under the A. A. A.* Washington, D.C.: The Brookings Institution, 1935, pp. 7 and 8.

point of view of a national agency entrusted with the responsibility for advancing as far as possible the prosperity of all the rival areas of production and of all the interrelated branches of agriculture. Since the interests of the producer, the processor, and the distributor are by no means identical and all of them may diverge more or less from other interests which must be within the concern of the Secretary of Agriculture, it is urged that this method of arriving at decisions involves a system of checks and balances which conduces to well-balanced decisions. Finally, the point is often made that since all the commodities in this group have a highly competitive market and since control devices are applicable only at certain spots within the field, attempts to use control to derive monopoly advantage rather than to guard against peculiar and in the main intermittent hazards of the industry are remote.

While the validity of this favorable view cannot be said to have been clearly established, the writer believes it is desirable that further experimentation with marketing agreements and orders as provided in the amended act be carried on to see what branches of agriculture they are technically applicable to and what possibilities this new development in our marketing institutions has for being used to the long-run advantage of farm producers. Whether devices calculated to bring this degree of prosperity to agricultural groups are economically dangerous to other classes is a question which is left to the concluding volume in this series.

These conclusions by Dr. Nourse were published in 1935. The experience with marketing agreements and orders since 1935 warrants the degree of optimism expressed in the above quotation. Marketing agreements and orders have two very important merits. First, unlike the various programs of production control and crop loans, marketing agreements and orders cost the taxpayer very little. Second, they are applicable to a number of perishable commodities that are not adaptable to regular price support programs of the Department of Agriculture.

As we see it, the main issues in the future of marketing agreements center upon two questions. First, should marketing agreements and orders be allowed for additional commodities not covered by present legislation? Second, should the scope of agreements be broadened to authorize a wider variety of marketing programs that seem to be in the interests of the producer and the general public? We think the answer to both questions is yes.

"Self-Help" Programs

From time to time there is revived interest in so-called "self-help" programs. One of the essential features of such programs is that the industry would bear most or all of the cost.

In this sense, at least, self-help programs include a variety of "certificate plans," such as those that have been advocated in recent years for wheat and rice. Producers would be given certificates covering their "fair share" of the domestic market. These certificates would have a stated monetary value. Processors of wheat or rice would have to buy certificates covering the amounts of these commodities that they sold in the domestic market for human food. Essentially this would be a two-price plan, with a higher price in the domestic food market and lower prices for domestic feed and for exports. Cochrane [3] recently proposed a program of national sales quotas for each principal agricultural commodity. This would be a more general form of certificate program.

Other industry groups, especially dairymen and turkey growers, have been advocating self-help marketing programs. Such programs would include features intended to discourage overproduction, to stabilize the principal domestic markets, to divert surpluses from normal channels of trade, and to develop new or expanded market outlets through research, advertising, and promotion.

These proposed programs would be carried out by industry boards, with some supervision by the Department of Agriculture. In principle, at least, these self-help marketing proposals have the same merits as marketing agreements and orders. As they are now being proposed, however, they raise certain

---

[3] Willard A. Cochrane, "An Appraisal of Recent Changes in Agricultural Programs in the United States," *Journal of Farm Economics*, May, 1957, pp. 297-298.

issues that need further study. Some of the questions being discussed are the following:

1. What authority, if any, should the Secretary of Agriculture have to overrule a commodity board?

2. Should commodity boards, with or without the consent of the Secretary, have the power to collect taxes (or fees) from producers and to determine the rate of taxation?

3. What, if any, authority should the board have to regulate production or to carry on foreign trade?

4. What authority, if any, should the board have to require producers to make payments to a fund to be used for research, advertising, and promotion?

The answers to these and similar questions are not clear. We do think it is important that no commodity board be allowed to carry out a marketing program, such as described in this chapter, without the consent and approval of some responsible public official or agency. It is at least possible that the present marketing agreement legislation might be broadened to authorize the main features of the self-help programs that are being advocated by such groups as the dairymen and the turkey producers.

QUESTIONS FOR DISCUSSION

1. Give reasons why Federal Marketing Orders should be abolished.

2. Give reasons why Federal Marketing Orders should be extended to all commodities in all parts of the country.

3. Could marketing orders be effective in regulating trade practices? In encouraging efficient marketing?

4. What market services provided by the government could be performed more satisfactorily by private industry?

SUPPLEMENTARY READING

1. Gordon, Leland J., *Economics for Consumers*. New York: American Book Company, 3rd ed., 1953, Ch. 25.
2. Shepherd, G. S., *Agricultural Price Policy*. Ames: Iowa State College Press, 1947, Chs. 6, 7, 8, and 9.
3. *Marketing, Yearbook of Agriculture, 1954*. Washington, D.C.: U. S. D. A., pp. 175-179.

27

Role of Government

Part 4 has outlined several kinds of government programs affecting agricultural marketing. But do not assume that all governments have the particular programs we have outlined —no more and no less. Actually, some governments have practically no marketing programs of any kind, while some other governments take a much more active hand in agricultural marketing than does our government.

Also, you will find great differences of opinion here in the United States about the proper size and scope of government programs in the field of agricultural marketing. Some think we have too much government in agricultural marketing— that we should place more reliance upon unregulated competition and free enterprise. Others advocate stronger government programs for such purposes as maintenance of farm income and protection of the consumer.

There is no final, authoritative, right answer to these issues. The best program for the United States might be totally unsuitable for Mexico or for Russia. A program that would have been adequate in 1900 might be quite inadequate today. An agricultural marketing program for ordinary peacetime might be inappropriate in wartime.

Therefore, a serious student will avoid any dogmatic position about the proper size and scope of government marketing programs. In this concluding chapter we shall note certain underlying trends and express some opinions concerning possible trends in the future. Our discussion will be mainly in terms of programs needed in ordinary peacetime.

Money, Weights, and Measures

In all but the most primitive countries, governments have taken the responsibility for coining money and for establishing and enforcing standards for weights and measures. Without such elementary measures, there can be little trade and therefore little improvement in levels of living. We need not dwell upon this here. Practically everyone in advanced countries agrees that governments should take responsibility for these matters.

Regulation of Trade Practices

Back in the Middle Ages, guilds were responsible for most regulation of trade practices. Even today, trade associations, boards of trade, commodity exchanges, and similar trade organizations continue to take some responsibility for enforcement of trade practices. However, in advanced countries more and more of this responsibility has been taken over by governments.

Most governments find it necessary to punish such dishonest practices as adulteration, misrepresentation, and short weighing. In the United States this includes enforcement of such Federal laws as the Packers and Stockyards Act, the Perishable Agricultural Commodities Act, and the Commodity Exchange Act. In addition, the courts enforce acts preventing restraint of trade and the disproportionate control of industries by one group which may provide them with a decided influence on price and market practices. Such regulations have sometimes met considerable opposition. Yet they have been continued and gradually strengthened. At present, in the United States, these programs seem to have become practically stabilized. There is no great pressure for more regulation of trade practices. On the other hand, any attempt to drop or to weaken present programs in this area would probably encounter vigorous opposition.

We believe that whenever any regulation of trade practice is needed, it should be done by local, state, or Federal governments rather than by the trade. Trade associations can, and often do, supplement the work of government agencies. But we think the main responsibility should rest with governments.

Marketing Services

The history of agricultural marketing throughout the world demonstrates the need for unbiased market news and statistics and for official grades and inspection. It is true that such services have sometimes been supplied by private concerns or by trade organizations. Private concerns ordinarily supply these services only to subscribers, and trade organizations provide them only for their members. Non-members, including farmers, are likely to doubt the accuracy and objectivity of trade information and services even if they have access to them. Before World War I, most of the market news and most of the grading in this country were handled by trade organizations or by private agencies. Now, Federal and state governments supply a great deal of detailed, up-to-date information concerning market conditions throughout the country. They also provide standard grades for practically all farm products and foods.

The Federal services of market news and grading have not completely supplanted the services provided by private agencies or trade organizations. Many trade organizations provide their members with additional market news. Also, many processors of farm products use their own private brands instead of government grades. A case in point is the grades for meat. The United States meat grades are permissive—that is, the meat packer may use them or not, as he pleases. Some of the largest packers prefer to stick with their private brands. The government meat grades make it possible for small packers (whose brands, if any, are not well-known) to compete on the basis of quality and grade. Sometimes the big packers object to this competition. For reasons of this kind, the trend toward more government grading and inspection has not been steadily upward. Yet, the setbacks to date have been few and temporary.

We think that government grading and inspection are badly needed in many of the less advanced countries. We think that permissive grades will be continued and probably strengthened somewhat in the United States. Compulsory labeling of foods is probably not needed, at least not in peacetime.

Domestic Economic Policy

Since the depression of the 1930's, many governments, including our own, have gone far beyond the kind of regulation and services we have just discussed. They have, for example, interfered in many ways with free market prices and with the free movement of farm products, both geographically and over time. This trend of the past 25 years may or may not prove to be permanent. At the present time there is much controversy, both in this country and abroad, concerning the proper role of government in economic policy generally. Some still say, "The best government is the least government." Actually, few of them would go so far. If they did, they would be anarchists, because the least government is no government at all.

We think one policy should be clear: If we are going to fix prices, it is much better to have them fixed by the government than to let them be fixed by corporations or by trade associations. The wave of misnamed "fair-trade" laws that have been passed by many states seem to us to run counter to this clear policy. The obvious effect is to suppress price competition with little, if any, government supervision.

To what extent should government fix prices or regulate prices in peacetime? This is a difficult question. The increase in size of marketing and production units increases the possibility of centralized economic power able to affect prices and supplies. For this reason, the government may be called upon to take a more positive role in pricing and in allocation of resources. We think there is need for government programs aimed at bringing about a reasonable degree of stability in the economy and at encouraging stable growth and prosperity. To some extent, we may be able to accomplish these ends by monetary measures. But we doubt that monetary measures alone will prove adequate to prevent major depressions. We think it would be wise to continue some kind of agricultural program aimed at maintaining a reasonable degree of stability in agricultural prices and farm income. This is not to say that we approve all aspects of the present program. The present program is a hodgepodge of all sorts of things—good and bad. But we don't go along with the notion held by some people, that because a program is expensive and not working well it should be completely junked. We suspect that most of the advanced countries will continue to have fairly active programs aimed at maintaining agricultural prices and farm incomes at levels that are thought to be in the interests of agriculture and the public generally.

Foreign Economic Policy

The experience of the United States, as well as that of many other countries, has demonstrated that strong agricultural programs are bound to have effects—for good or ill—upon foreign trade. For many years the United States has supported prices of principal farm products at levels higher than world prices. To do this, we have had to take positive steps both to promote exports and to discourage imports.

Since World War II, our export programs have undoubtedly greatly benefited some foreign countries whose food supplies were short. Yet, as we encourage exports, either by direct or indirect subsidies, we may naturally encounter some opposition from farmers in other parts of the world.

Like most economists, the authors of this book are in favor of the general principle of free international trade. Yet, we think it is realistic to believe that completely free trade is a long way off. For many years, at least, both the important agricultural producing countries and the important food-importing countries will undoubtedly continue to have many import duties, quotas, monetary restrictions, open or hidden subsidies, and other departures from free international trade. In this situation, we think the best hope lies in some form of international agreements, rather than in unilateral action by individual governments. Perhaps Sir John Orr was too visionary in his proposal for a World Food Board. Perhaps a more workable substitute may be something like the International Wheat Agreement. In any case, we expect and certainly hope that the trend will be toward more consultation and co-operation in the international aspects of agricultural marketing.

Index

A

Advertising, 96-97, 101-103, 109
  cigarette, 124
  and economic growth, 111
  and health, 111-12
  see also Brands, Promotion
A.F.L. (American Federation of Labor), 199
Agreements:
  commodity, internation, 253-54
  marketing, 154, 257-62
  price, 203-04
Agricultural Adjustment Act, 259
Agricultural Adjustment Administration, 259
Agricultural Marketing Act, 259
Agricultural Marketing Agreement Act, 259
Agricultural Marketing Service, 248
Agriculture, United States Department of, 8-9, 24, 48, 156, 159, 161, 189, 193, 211, 217, 246, 260, 262
Aims:
  of consumers, 14
  of economic life, 4-6
  of farmers, 4, 13
  of governmental marketing programs, 210-11
  of governmental storage, 237
  of groups, 6-7, 181-82
  of handlers, 4, 13-14, 33
  of the individual, 4-6, 63
  of society, 6, 60
  of the study of agricultural marketing, 3-12, 13
Alcohol, grain, 155
Allocation:
  of food supplies, 52-53
  market, 17-18, 114-123
  of resources, 58-60

American Dairy Association, 107, 182, 199
American Farm Bureau Federation, 196
A & P (Atlantic & Pacific Tea Co.), 126
Apples, 21, 72, 102-103, 116, 140, 143, 148-49, 167, 171, 220-21
Argentine, 253
Arkansas Agricultural Wheel, 188
Aroostook County, Maine, 65
Asparagus, 125
Australia, 253

B

Baltimore (Md.), 128
Barley, 19
Beef, 19, 67, 72, 220
  consumer demand for, 92-99
  see also Meat
Black, John D., 62, 64-65
Boredom, 63
Boston (Mass.), 71, 125, 245
Brands, 103, 106-107, 108, 192, 201
  multiple-line, 105
British Empire, 258
Broiler processing, 35, 79
Brothers of Freedom, 188
Budget-making, 51, 66
Buffalo (N.Y.), 71
Bureau of Agricultural Economics, 213
Business cycles, 144

C

California, 16, 21, 52, 135, 153, 188
California Fruit Growers Exchange, 188, 193
Canada, 82, 253

269